AN APPETITE FOR LIFE:CREATE A LIFE FREE FROM BINGE EATING AND BULIMIA

First edition published 2021

Copyright © 2021 by Tony Henshall

Published by
Dr Tony Henshall

Manchester
Uk
https://drtonyhenshall.com

Publishers note: This book is to provide information on the subject matter and is not intended as a substitute for medical advice of a physician. The reader should regularly consult a physician in matters relating to his or her health and particularly with respect to any symptoms that may require diagnosis or medical attention.

I have changed the names used in the quotes and examples for reasons of client confidentiality.

Thank you to my clients, who have taught me so much

Author photograph provided by Senem Peace Photography

Book Mentoring and Editing by Siân-Elin Flint Freel

Cover design, and interior formatting provided by Natalie McLetchie

Paperback ISBN 978-1-8384808-0-6
Ebook ISBN 978-1-8384808-1-3

FOR MY PARTNER, KAREN

Without her constant chivvying along, this book would still be an idea that I wanted to get around to at some time in the future.

CO

WHAT PEOPLE SAY ABOUT MY
RECOVERY COURSE: "APPETITE FOR LIFE"

'I REMEMBER SAYING AT OUR FIRST MEETING THAT I'D FORGOTTEN HOW TO EAT NORMALLY, I DIDN'T KNOW HOW TO EAT, I DIDN'T KNOW WHAT WAS RIGHT ANYMORE. YOU'VE SHOWN ME HOW TO FEED AND NOURISH MY BODY AND TRUST MY BODY AGAIN. IT IS POSSIBLE TO CHANGE. I FOLLOWED WHAT YOU SAID, HOWEVER ALIEN IT FELT TO ME, AND WHAT D'YA KNOW, THAT SHIT WORKS!'
FIONA

'IT'S ACTUALLY DIFFICULT TO PUT INTO WORDS THE PHENOMENAL IMPACT THAT YOUR SESSIONS HAVE HAD ON ME. I NEVER IMAGINED I'D BE WHERE I AM NOW AFTER YEARS OF SELF-ABUSE AND SELF-HATRED.

'THE UNCONTROLLABLE BINGES ON FOOD CONTROLLED MY LIFE AND I HATED MYSELF FOR NOT HAVING (WHAT I THOUGHT WAS) 'WILLPOWER' TO CHANGE. LOVING MYSELF SEEMED QUITE OFTEN AN IMPOSSIBLE TASK. ALL I DESIRED WAS TO BE FREE, FREE FROM MY DEPRESSING OBSESSION WITH FOOD, FREE FROM THE GUILT AND FREE FROM THE DAMAGE I WAS DOING TO MY BODY.

'AND THAT'S EXACTLY WHAT YOU'VE GIVEN ME. FREEDOM.

'YOU'VE FLIPPED MY MINDSET COMPLETELY. NOT ONLY WHERE FOOD IS CONCERNED BUT MY HAPPINESS FOR LIFE TOO. WITHIN A FEW SHORT WEEKS I STARTED TO BELIEVE IN MYSELF AND MY ABILITY TO HEAL AND BUILD A HEALTHY RELATIONSHIP WITH FOOD.'
GEMMA

"I BOOKED AN APPOINTMENT WITH TONY THINKING I HAD TRIED ABSOLUTELY EVERYTHING. I HAD BEEN BATTLING SEVERE BULIMIA FOR TWO AND A HALF YEARS AND TRIED BUT FAILED MANY TIMES TO STOP. I WAS DESPERATE TO CHANGE. THE ILLNESS WAS CONSUMING MY LIFE AND HAVING A DETRIMENTAL EFFECT ON MY HEALTH.

"I MET WITH TONY AND AFTER THE FIRST APPOINTMENT REALISED HE UNDERSTOOD MORE THAN MY COUNSELLOR HAD MANAGED TO UNDERSTAND IN A YEAR. HE TAUGHT ME SO MUCH ABOUT AN ILLNESS THAT HAD TAKEN OVER MY LIFE AND HELPED ME REALISE FOR THE FIRST TIME I COULD BEAT THIS.

"AFTER MY SECOND SESSION I WAS ABLE TO CONTROL A VOICE THAT HAD CONSUMED MY LIFE FOR SO LONG AND I FINALLY FELT LIKE I HAD MY OWN VOICE COMING BACK. FOR SOMEONE WHO HADN'T MANAGED MORE THAN TWO DAYS WITHOUT A BULIMIA CYCLE IN TWO AND A HALF YEARS, AFTER MY SECOND SESSION I'M AMAZED AT HOW I'VE MANAGED TO CONTROL THE URGE AND GET INTO A PATTERN OF REGULAR EATING." JANE

"TONY'S SUPPORT HAS BEEN AMAZING AND I CAN'T PUT INTO WORDS HOW HE HAS NOT ONLY GIVEN ME THE TOOLS TO FIX MY PROBLEM, HE'S GIVEN ME THE REALISATION THAT I FINALLY CAN HAVE MY LIFE BACK AND CAN BEAT THIS FOREVER.

"THANK YOU SO MUCH, TONY, I DEFINITELY FEEL A LOT BETTER NOW. I REALLY APPRECIATE ALL OF YOUR SUPPORT AND PATIENCE." SARAH

READY TO READ ON...?

INTRODUCTION

You are in the right place if:

- you have been battling with bulimia or binge eating, have tried everything and now you are simply sick and tired of it.

- you're fed up of constantly obsessing about what you should be eating, what you have just eaten, what you wish you had eaten, how are you going to cope at the party, etc. But, most of all,

- you are fed up of wasting all that time, money and energy and you want to take back control of your life and focus on the things you were put on this earth to achieve.

I know that you have probably tried time and time again to put this problem behind you. You probably think you have tried everything. You might even think that there is something wrong with you when you hear about other people recovering. But, somehow you just can't seem to get this part of your life in control. Picking up this book is proof that you are still looking to beat this thing so well done you!

The first thing to understand is that having an eating disorder does not mean you are weak-willed or lack discipline. On the contrary, most of my clients share very positive characteristics. They are all, without exception:

Living with high standards

Disciplined

Focused

With perfectionist tendencies

Capable of delaying gratification - enduring short-term pain for long term gain

Intelligent

Able to finish what they start

With these characteristics, it's not surprising that my clients achieve a great deal of success in all aspects of their lives – except when it comes to food. It comes as a mystery to them that when the urge to binge strikes, it's almost like someone else takes over and they seem powerless to fight it, no matter how hard they try. And boy, do they try!

If this rings any bells with you, the first step is to stop beating yourself up. It's not your fault. Bulimia and binge eating are very complex conditions. You've probably been using what seemed like good ways to recover and the most logical course of action to get back in control. But the sad fact is, in many cases, these are the very actions that keep your eating disorder firmly in place. The harder you try using these methods, the more you entrench your condition. So, don't beat yourself up for not trying hard enough, you've probably been trying too hard. It's now time to try something different. Something that works.

BUT HOW DO YOU KNOW WHAT WORKS?

There is lots of information out there, but where do you start? The problem is that there is a lot of simplistic, misinformed and even dangerous advice out there and it's difficult to know what to do for the best. The good news is that a great deal of research has taken place over the years and we have a good scientifically based understanding of both bulimia and binge eating.

We Know:

- how binge eating and bulimia start.

- how they become embedded in your life and, most importantly,

- we know how to make them stop.

Using this knowledge and with a little help you will soon be back in control, building a good relationship with food and enjoying the pleasure that it can bring.

WHO THIS BOOK IS FOR

APPETITE FOR LIFE is for people who want to gain the insights, skills and techniques that will help them to recover. Their recovery often sets in motion a process of personal growth that will enhance the rest of their lives.

It is a recovery programme for people who:

- feel out of control around food and want to take back that control.

- want to free their mind from obsessing about food all day, every day, mentally counting the calories in everything they eat, what they don't eat, and what somebody else eats

- are fed up of all those rigid rules that dictate what they can and cannot eat.

- have become tired of keeping secrets and deceiving the people they love.

- feel guilty all the time, fed up of feeling like an imposter who will be 'found out' every time they achieve something.

- loathe wasting all that money, time and energy on something they hate.

- want to get their life back so they can put all their energies into something worthwhile that will make them and their loved ones proud.

I used to hate being invited out for a meal.
I would need at least a week's notice. I would
look up the restaurant and go through the menu
with a fine-tooth comb, to decide what I
could and couldn't eat. Then working out th
calories in everything on the menu, guessing
what everybody would eat and working out how
many calories they would eat and on and on.

I would spend the week cutting back to make
up for the food. I would eat, constantly
weighing myself and feel awful. Basically, I would
totally obsessed by it and it would take over
my life for the whole week."

Jean

READY, WILLING BUT NOT QUITE ABLE

Your chances of recovering from an eating disorder depends on three things:
Are you ready, willing and able to recover?

- **READY**   Are you at the stage where you are motivated to change?

- **WILLING**   Are you willing to put that motivation into action and take those first steps to change?

- **ABLE**   Do you have the knowledge and skills to recover successfully? Do you have the food knowledge, mental clarity and emotional resilience to put into practice the changes in behaviour that will lead to full recovery?

By picking up this book you have shown that you are ready and willing, but for various reasons are not yet able to recover from your eating disorder. I have written this book as a recovery programme, so that step by step you will gain all the knowledge and skills you will need. With your readiness and willingness, along with my knowledge and guidance, you will be able to make a real difference to your life.

FRIENDS AND FAMILY OF A PERSON WITH AN EATING DISORDER

You may have a good relationship with food but you worry about someone who has an eating disorder and want to help them. In which case, they will need to be motivated and willing to change for any action to be a success, but you can help. Using the knowledge you gain from this book, and the enhanced clarity you will have about their condition, you will be able to give them the emotional support they need to help them to recover.

WHAT MAKES THIS BOOK DIFFERENT?

WHAT MAKES THIS BOOK DIFFERENT?

At first sight, there are lots of books out there that hold out the promise of helping you on your road to recovery. They seem to fall into two broad categories: personal recovery journeys or academic/medical books. Both are very interesting in their way, but not that useful to your recovery.

Personal recovery journeys usually take the form of 'I had bulimia, I hit rock-bottom, look how bad I was, and, after a long, hard fight, I'm fully recovered. If I was so bad and I can recover, so can you.' These accounts are often cathartic to the author and can be enlightening to the reader. But they are just that, a 'personal recovery journey' which applies specifically to the author. While these might show you that recovery is possible, they describe how the author recovered, but they will not necessarily show you how to recover.

The fact is that you are not them, you don't have the same background, experiences, or support as they do. Worse of all, they may attribute their recovery to something quite random that just happened at the same time all the stars aligned to help them get better.

For example, they may feel that beginning a new relationship was the turning point that gave them the extra motivation they needed to stop bingeing. Well, maybe this was the case, but it could have been the changes in the way they ate with their new partner or that they took better care of themselves or any of a myriad of small changes that a new relationship brings. It could be that any one of these changes was the key factor, or the culmination of all the changes that led to recovery. In such cases, it is very difficult to put your finger on what helped the person recover and there is no guarantee what worked for them would work for you. You are probably not at the same place in your journey as them. So, if you try to do what worked for them and it doesn't work for you it can be extremely dispiriting and make you feel that something is wrong with you – it's not, by the way. These personal journey books may help you realise that other people have had the same problems as you and were successful in getting better. They might give you some insights, but they will not be the key to your recovery.

The second category of books tends to take a more academic look at eating disorders and are written for a professional audience. There is lots of good stuff in these books, but they tend to be very dry, and quite frankly you will have to endure a very steep learning curve before they will be useful in your recovery.

These books lay down the scientific and medical basis for eating disorders recovery. The problem is that eating disorders recovery need a multi-disciplinary approach and these books tend to cover separate specialist areas. One book might explain how food is digested and used in the body, how restrictive diets slow metabolism and the consequent effect on hormone production and neuro transmitters. Another might discuss the effects of different mindsets, while another investigates emotional resilience or body image etc.

There is simply so much to learn before you can put any of it into practice. I find these works fascinating and have spent many years reading around my subject, but the question is, do you want to? Have you got the time and stamina to climb that steep learning curve? If you are like most of my clients, you simply want the eating disorder to STOP and stop now. My clients only want to learn what they need to know to recover and to get on with their lives. In effect, I've done the reading, so you don't have to.

THE RECOVERY PROGRAMME:
EVERYTHING YOU NEED TO KNOW TO RECOVER

APPETITE FOR LIFE is based on the recovery programme that I have designed for my private clients. The programme is constructed on the best medical evidence, as well as my years of experience in what works. It is also shaped by the 'Integrated Eating Disorders' model pioneered by The National Centre for Eating Disorders and uses a combination of nutritional rehabilitation, psychotherapy and visualisation techniques.

Taking you step by step to a full recovery, this book contains all the knowledge, skills and techniques that you will need to recover, plus make the process as easy as possible.

The first stage in this model will set you up to succeed by stabilising your body with nourishing food. I know that this might be an issue to some of you, but bear with me. Once you have read the chapter on food knowledge you will realise how vital this is to your recovery. Of course, we are talking about huge changes and there will be days when things don't quite work out, so I will teach you how to deal with lapses early on in the programme by using relapse recovery techniques. These will get you back on course as quickly as possible and will help you gain the confidence to succeed.

There are emotional aspects to eating disorders, such as stress, anxiety and poor body image. Even the way you think about food can affect how you behave ('I've blown it – might as well eat everything!'). The programme includes the skills and techniques needed to break these old habits and will help you find new, better ways of solving your problems and handling stress.

THE BOOK IS LAID OUT IN THREE MAIN SECTIONS:

Section One : How eating disorders develop

- Why this programme works for both binge eating and bulimia.
- The three risk factors of developing an eating disorder.
- The physical and emotional factors that keep it in place.
- How you are personally affected by your eating disorder.
- The effect of food chaos.
- Food knowledge: how to work with your body instead of against it.

This section is a lot to take on – but stick with it and it will form the firm foundation of your recovery.

Section Two : How to recover from your eating disorder

An eating disorder is kept in place by a combination of physical and psychological factors. This section deals with them one at a time.

- Physical factors – The first step is to deal with the physical side of the problem, ending food chaos by stabilising your blood sugar levels. **This will dramatically reduce many of your symptoms.**

- Critical voice – A key factor is that critical voice in your head. You will learn techniques to shut it up.

- Habit – A large part of the condition is simply habit. You will learn habit-breaking techniques which will gently replace unhelpful habits with positive life-affirming habits.

- Stress – Discover techniques to help you gain control over the parts of your life which are causing you the most stress.

- Emotions – Understand how to handle uncomfortable emotions in ways that do not involve food.

- Perfectionist tendencies – Ironically, when you learn to become more flexible, you will gain more control over your life.

- Poor body image – Learn how to be more comfortable in your own skin.

Section Three: Living in recovery

- Relapse prevention and rapid recovery.
- How to help friends and relatives with eating disorders.
- Dealing with 'real-world problems'.
- Getting the best help from your GP.

I know you might be in a dark place at the moment. I also know that when you have the knowledge to work with your body (and not against it) and have learned new skills, you can soon turn that around.

Within a short space of time following this programme, you'll notice a remarkable reduction in your urges to binge. You will have the skills to:

- switch off triggers;
- shut-up that annoying voice in your head;
- stop obsessing about food; and most importantly,
- begin to love living in your own skin and get on with your life.

HOW TO
USE THIS
BOOK

THIS IS NOT A TEXT BOOK

From my experience in the NHS I am convinced that people in pain are not that interested in theories about why they are in pain – they just want it to stop. This is the ethos of my practice and it is also the main thrust of the book. I am not really interested in why you have an eating disorder and I am not really interested in how it developed. But I am very interested in helping you to fully recover and put this nightmare firmly behind you. My book has everything you need to know to set yourself up for success and recover.

BASED IN THE REAL LIVED EXPERIENCES OF CLIENTS WHO RECOVERED

I have based this book on the real life experiences of my clients who have recovered. To protect their privacy I have used pseudonyms throughout. Their thoughts during recovery are scattered throughout the book. Real answers they have given are shown to help you complete the exercises. I am sure that you will recognise yourself in their words and their pain as they start on the journey will resonate with you. As you work through the book, let their spirit to embrace change inspire you to join them and to fully recover and flourish.

'BITESIZE'

In some of the chapters there is a lot to take in as you unpick years, or even decades of misinformation. Don't worry, just take your time and let it sink in.

At the end of each chapter will be a section called 'bitesize' where the key points are summarised. This will give you the chance to check whether you have really taken on board what you have read. If not, simply re-read the chapter. Each chapter builds on the previous one, so it is really important that you understand fully before moving on to the next chapter. It's also a great summary if you want to check back at any time.

'WHAT I HAVE LEARNED'

At the end of each chapter there is a place for you to make notes of what you have learned. This is really helpful when you are reviewing what you have learned in previous chapters. It is an opportunity for you to explore your feelings in relation to what you have just read. Feel free to express yourself in whatever way seems best to you.

EXERCISES

Throughout the book are exercises for you to do. I explain each exercise and then give you a real life example of how a client has filled it in. You can then do the exercise. Once done I will show you how to interpret what you have written. You can write your insights of what your answers are telling you in the 'what I have learned' section.

TECHNIQUES

There are lots of techniques throughout the book. I have chosen these carefully because I know they work and they will really help you recover. There is an added benefit in that these techniques are transferable skills and once learned they will serve you well in other situations for the rest of you life.

Time to jump into the book.

Begin to LOVE living in your skin
and get on with your life

MIRACLE QUESTION

Now it is time to concentrate on your hopes for recovery. What would life be like once this is far behind you? Some of my clients find this very difficult to answer, and you might as well. So, before we go any further, I'll ask you what is known as the miracle question:

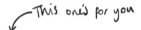 This one's for you

If I could wave a magic wand and your eating disorder vanished, what would your life be like? What would you be doing? Where would you be going and with who? How would you feel? What would you be wearing? What would be different?

Write the answer to this question in the box below. Spend a little time on it because it will prove very important in future techniques that we will explore.

IF YOU WAVED A MAGIC WAND AND MY EATING
DISORDER VANISHED, I WOULD BE...

THE ELEPHANT IN THE ROOM

Before we go any further, it's important to tackle the elephant in the room. Many of my clients want the pain of the eating disorder to go away, but would also like to lose weight at the same time. The problem is that your chances of stopping bingeing while you are still trying to lose weight are nil. Any progress you make towards recovery will be undermined by any attempt at dieting. I know that this is the last thing that you want to hear, but nevertheless it is true. It seems like giving up on your weight loss dreams, but is it?

Ask yourself:

Do you think you will lose any weight while you are still bingeing?

It might take a little while, but eventually you will have to admit it – you will never lose weight while you are bingeing.

To put that more clearly:

- **YOU WILL NEVER LOSE WEIGHT WHILE YOU ARE BINGEING.**

- **YOUR CHANCES OF STOPPING BINGEING WHILE TRYING TO LOSE WEIGHT ARE – NIL.**

It is important we are crystal clear – your priority is to recover from your eating disorder.

TWO-STAGE APPROACH TO RECOVERY

I understand that this seems like being between a rock and a hard place, but it's not. Let me show you how. The best way to move forward is by thinking of medium- and long-term goals that we can both agree on.

Trust me, it works!

"When Tony first told me this, I was desperate to change, but was very frightened of putting on weight. I didn't tell Tony, but I thought once I stopped bingeing I would then set about losing weight. But I was worrying for nothing: once I no longer needed to binge, my body stabalised & so did my weight."

Susan

STAGE ONE
Binge eating and bulimia recovery

Your immediate goal is to recover from your eating disorder. We are not concerned with weight loss at this stage. Although, when my clients stop binge eating, most lose weight. This book concentrates on the medium-term goal, showing you how to recover from bulimia or binge eating.

STAGE TWO
You can decide this, once you have recovered

After recovering from binge eating, you will have a better understanding of how to work with your body and you will have learned many new personal growth skills and techniques. You will have a calm body, be able to think more clearly and have greater emotional resilience. Once you have successfully recovered from your eating disorder, you will be in a better place to decide your long-term goal.

For now, we will concentrate on helping you recover from bingeing and you can think about the next steps when you are in a better place to decide.

If you see bingeing as an annoying obstacle that is getting in the way of you losing weight, or if you are looking for a silver bullet to take away the bingeing so you can lose more weight, then this book is not for you. Both binge eating and bulimia are complex conditions which, if left alone, will get increasingly worse and take over your life – if it hasn't already.

Please be honest with yourself. If your aim is to stop bingeing so that you can get on with your weight loss plan, then this book is not for you – at this moment in time. Unfortunately, you will have to go through a lot more pain until you are ready to recover. Deep down you know what you are doing now will never achieve your goal and you will be making yourself miserable trying. Make a note of this book and come back when you are ready to make changes.

This book is for people who want to stop bingeing full stop, for people who want to stop binge eating and take back control of their lives, and for people with bulimia who realise that it they stop bingeing they would not need to purge.

SCARY OR WHAT?

Giving up your plan to lose weight can feel extremely scary. But ask yourself this: has what you are doing worked? If you are reading this book, I am willing to bet that you have been on diet after diet in the hope of losing weight only to rebound and regain any weight you lost and probably more.

Most serial dieters are either dieting/restricting (and therefore feel in control) or believe they are bingeing out of control. I suspect that for many of you this is a pattern you have experienced throughout your life. But, as you will soon find out, this does not have to be your future. The opposite of dieting is NOT being out of control, eating anything and everything.

Just because you can eat anything, doesn't mean you have to eat everything.

The opposite of dieting is eating normally. By that, I mean eating enough to healthily nourish your body. Putting food in its right place in your life – a simple pleasure. Eating when you are hungry and stopping when you feel full, eating for enjoyment and, for the rest of the time, food not even crossing your mind.

I know that you will find this hard to believe at the moment, but I have designed this book to take you, step by step, along the recovery programme I follow with clients that leads them (and will lead you) to being in control and happy around food.

A LITTLE BIT ABOUT MYSELF...

WHY I NOW WORK IN BULIMIA AND BINGE EATING RECOVERY

I have thought long and hard about why, of all the areas I could have chosen to work, I am instinctively drawn to the area of eating disorders.

I think it's just the unfairness of the situation.

- It's unfair that we are consistently being bombarded with unrealistic body images that nobody (including the models in the photographs) can attain and then we are told that is what we are supposed to look like.

- It's unfair that we have been told the way to lose weight is to diet – the very method that is almost certainly guaranteed to make you gain weight. Then, when the inevitable rebound weight gain occurs, we blame ourselves and not the method for failure.

- It's unfair that people with the characteristics of discipline and willpower, who are trying to do the very best they can, that these same characteristics can spiral into an eating disorder and keep it firmly in place for what can be years. Such people have the willpower to restrict their diet harder, exercise harder and stick at it for longer. When the inevitable happens, they fall harder and have much deeper feelings of failure which, in turn, inspires them to diet, exercise even harder, and so the vicious cycle starts again, spiraling down.

Sounds a bit gloomy. But I also know that with help you can fully recover from your eating disorder. The road to complete recovery is not difficult – the difficulty is getting people with an eating disorder to start along the road while they still hold the beliefs that unrealistic body shapes are achievable, that dieting will make them thin and, when they fail, it is their own fault because they have not used enough discipline and willpower.

Unpicking decades of mis-information is always a challenge. However, seeing clients visibly bloom within a few weeks as they see that recovery is both possible and achievable makes it all worthwhile.

I know your eating disorder can seem very complex, difficult to understand and the idea of recovery is a faraway dream.

- we understand what causes eating disorders.
- we understand how they continue and can spiral out of control.
- we understand how they can become an obsession that totally overtakes your life and, most importantly,
- we know how to help you achieve a complete recovery.

But the truth is, medically:

- we understand what causes eating disorders.

- we understand how they continue and can spiral out of control.

- we understand how they can become an obsession that totally overtakes your life and, most

We Know how to HELP you
ACHIEVE a complete RECOVERY

SO, LET'S GET STARTED.

SECTION ONE

HOW EATING DISORDERS DEVELOP

CHAPTER ONE

CONGRATULATIONS

First of all, I would like to say well done for looking for help.

I know that you have probably tried time and time again to put this thing behind you. You probably think you have tried everything. You might even think that there is something wrong with you when you hear about other people recovering, but somehow you just can't seem to get this part of your life under control. So, it's a big step to get this far, to realise that there is so much more to life and to decide that you are willing to do whatever it takes to live your life to its full potential.

Don't worry about past attempts; bulimia and binge eating are very complex conditions. You've probably been experimenting with what you've heard are good ways to recover and what seems like the most logical course of action to get back in control, but the sad fact is, in many cases, these are the very actions that are keeping your condition firmly in place.

The good news is that both bulimia and binge eating are well understood and, with a little help, you will soon be back in control, building a good relationship with food and enjoying all the pleasure that it can bring. I know this may seem like an impossible dream at this stage, but I know the impact that my programme has had and have seen the astounding results.

Section 1 can be a little difficult because it contains a lot of food knowledge and dispels a lot of misinformation about food and weight. It will also explain how you got to where you are at the moment, and more importantly give you the scientific information you need for a strong foundation for your recovery. It might be a bit heavy, but don't skip this section.

Before we start on the programme, it is important for you have some background knowledge on what binge eating and bulimia have in common.

why this programme works for both binge eating & bulimia

I am often asked how the same recovery programme can work for both bulimia and binge eating. At first sight they seem like very different eating disorders which you would expect to be treated differently:

- People who binge eat want to recover by stopping bingeing.

- People with bulimia want to recover by stopping purging (vomiting, use of laxatives, over-exercising).

The difference is that binge eaters know their problem is bingeing. Binge eaters see their problem as:

'dieting' > oh no! binge > diet harder to make up for the binge

Bingeing is stopping them from losing weight and, in many cases, causing them to gain weight. They want to stop bingeing.

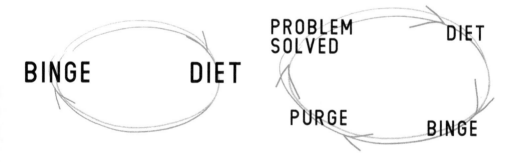

Whereas people with bulimia (at first) feel they have solved their bingeing problem. They are wrong, of course, but at least initially they see the situation as:

'Dieting' > Oh No! Binge > Purge > Problem Solved > 'Dieting'

If you ask people with bulimia why they purge, the vast majority will tell you that they purge because they had binged. If you asked them if they get the urge to purge if they don't binge, again, the vast majority would say 'no'.

What we see in the behaviour of binge eaters and people with bulimia in the same underlying problem – bingeing. The only difference is that people with bulimia initially think (but soon realise that they were very wrong) that they have solved the problem of bingeing by purging.

Bulimia brings its own set of problems, so I have included a chapter which discusses this subject.

BOTH HAVE THE SAME PROBLEM

To reinforce my point, both binge eating and people with bulimia have the same problem – 'bingeing'. If both groups could stop bingeing they would be 'cured'. The binge eaters would have recovered because they no longer binge, people with bulimia who stop bingeing would have no need to purge and so would also have recovered. Therefore, the solution to both is to stop binge eating, and this programme will concentrate on how to do just that.

> 'OK, Tony,' you might say, 'that's very easy for you to say but don't you think I've tried everything over the years to stop bingeing? Surely, if there was a way, I would have found it by now?'

Well, there is a way to stop bingeing, and if you know where to look you can find it. The problem is that it is hidden in medical text books which are not very accessible, whereas the stuff that keeps you firmly entrapped in your eating disorder is in the spotlight, everywhere.

It has become part of the society in which we live. Everywhere we look we see people pushing diet culture and the cult of thinness. They fill the airways, appear on talk shows and are all over our newspapers, presenting themselves as experts, peddling their latest 'silver bullet' to make you thin, and advertising their special ingredients etc. They are so plausible and appear on highly respected television shows, so it's no surprise that people look to them for help.

It's like the old joke about the drunk on his knees in the gutter looking for his wallet. A stranger asks him what he is doing. He says he has spent hours looking up and down this gutter for his wallet but can't find it. The stranger asks where was the last place he had his wallet and the drunk says on the other side of the street. The stranger says, 'Why don't you look over there?' and the drunk replies, 'The light is much brighter on this side of the street.'

There is a great deal of light on the side of the street that keeps a person locked in an eating disorder – full of shiny people who know how to get publicity and will push anything in order to make money, with no thought of the devastation they leave in their wake. These people are part of the problem and therefore cannot be part of the solution.

The solution lies on 'the other side of the street'. That quiet side of the street that is made up of people who know about nutrition, psychological disorders, and are experts in eating disorders – people who actually know what they are talking about.

It might come as a surprise, but we know how people develop binge eating and bulimia, and also how they maintain and recover from them. The problem is that learning this knowledge is a steep learning curve across a number of disciplines. This book will make this learning curve as smooth as possible for you. I will take you on the step by step programme I take my clients through. Each step towards recovery builds on the previous step and will feel positive benefits that will build your confidence and resilience, and lead to personal growth.

IT'S NOT YOUR FAULT

To most of my clients their bulimia and binge eating is something of a mystery. They hate it, they hate what it does to them, and they hate how it makes them feel, both physically and emotionally. They hate how obsessing about food gets in the way of important parts of their life. They hate the secrecy and deceiving people they love – just to indulge in something they hate. They hate the money it costs and how it undermines their self-esteem in every area of their lives. The things they hate goes on and on. But most of all, they hate the fact that no matter what they try or how hard they try, they appear to be powerless to do anything about it.

And that is scary, very scary.

The first thing that you must know about your eating disorder is that it's simply not your fault. Or, more accurately, it's not all your fault. At a certain level, we must all take responsibility for our actions.

But if you (like my clients) do your best to become the best person you can be and, when you fail, pull yourself together and try even harder again and again to achieve the best you can be, are you really at fault? Even when the results take a downward spiral into an eating disorder and you keep on trying harder and harder, are you really at fault?

Well you may get a 'A for effort', but the fact is that (quite understandably) you have fallen for a set of lies (like most of us), such as 'being underweight is healthy' (no it isn't) or 'dieting is a good way of losing weight' (no it isn't). These lies are built into our culture and we mistake them for facts.

In order to recover, you will need the knowledge to be able to separate the truth from the lies.

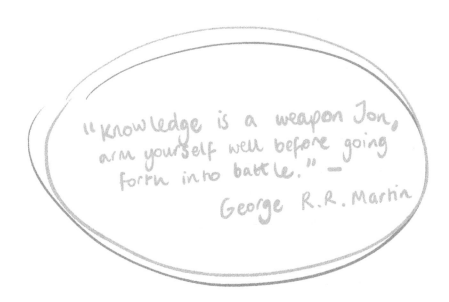

"Knowledge is a weapon Jon, arm yourself well before going forth into battle." — George R.R. Martin

Once you have armed yourself with knowledge, you will understand what keeps your eating disorder so firmly in place. This knowledge and the 'ah-ha – I'm not mad/stupid/weak after all – that's why' moment will be a great boost to your self-esteem and confidence. But, more importantly, this knowledge will provide the sound basis of your recovery, so you can take back control of your life, turn food into a pleasure and get on with something important.

THE THREE RISK FACTORS OF DEVELOPING AN EATING DISORDER

There is no specific cause of an eating disorder as such, only risk factors that make a person susceptible to developing one. Individually, these risks are relatively benign, but when they occur together they can be devastating to the life of the sufferer.

In the literature, these are called the 3 Ps:

PREDISPOSITION (CHARACTERISTICS):
SOME ARE MORE SUSCEPTIBLE.

Some people are more susceptible than others to developing an eating disorder. This is not a character fault, but the qualities that allow them to achieve so much in other parts of their lives, such as sensitivity, intelligence, determination, strong willpower, the ability to focus on a single thing and the perseverance to press ahead with a task. These positive characteristics, unfortunately, make a person particularly vulnerable.

PRECIPITATING:
SOMETHING HAPPENS TO 'KICK OFF' THE EATING DISORDER.

Something happens (this could be bullying, teasing, puberty, weight gain, etc.) which causes a person with a predisposition to go on a restrictive diet. And, being who they are, they put all their skills and determination into dieting. They become the 'best dieter ever'. As they lose weight, they get a great deal of adulation and attention. This inspires them to press on and diet 'harder'. When they inevitably crash, being sensitive they feel the pain all the greater and then try again with more determination. Unfortunately, dieting like this can easily spiral into an eating disorder.

PERPETUATING:
VARIOUS THINGS KEEP THE EATING DISORDER FIRMLY IN PLACE.

A number of physical and psychological/ emotional factors keep the eating disorder firmly in place. Factors such as:

- food chaos
- habit
- payoffs
- emotions
- poor body image
- thinking styles

These factors keep the sufferer locked into their eating disorder.

All of the 3 Ps are needed for an eating disorder to start, become embedded and to be maintained over years or even decades

STRATEGY FOR EATING DISORDER RECOVERY

Given there is no cause of an eating disorder, how will you recover?

You can't change your personality, and why should you? You have many great skills and qualities. That said, you can add a few more tools to your toolkit.

You can't change whatever kicked off the eating disorder – it's in the past. You can't change the past, so leave it back there and move on (it's simply not worth your thoughts). In the recovery programme, we won't be spending time on uncovering deep psychological reasons for why you developed an eating disorder. My clients simply want to know how to recover from their condition and I am assuming you do as well. The focus will be on giving you the knowledge, skills and techniques to recover.

But something can be done about the things that are maintaining the eating disorder. By removing the factors that keep your condition in place it will become less and less relevant to your life and, as it fades away, you will recover.

So, let's get started with your recovery.

BITESIZE

You have taken your first steps to recovery and you now know the following:

• Why this recovery programme works for both bulimia and binge eating.
• It is not really your fault.
• The risk factors of developing an eating disorder.
• How the programme is set out to help you recover.

Remember, if you are still unsure about any of the above, then just read this chapter again before you move on.

This one's for you

WHAT I LEARNED... WHAT I WILL DO...

CHAPTER TWO

HOW YOU ARE AFFECTED BY YOUR EATING DISORDER

It is important to get a good understanding of how your eating disorder is affecting your life. Often my clients are so wrapped up in the daily turmoil of their eating disorder that they do not have time to reflect on how it is impacting on their and their loved ones' lives. Spending a few moments considering this now will set out a good baseline of where you are starting, from which you can recognise the progress you are making as you continue through the programme.

In order to find out how an eating disorder affects individual clients I send them a **pre-meeting questionnaire.**

These questions give me an overall understanding of what the client is bringing to the first consultation, what they hope to achieve and some key areas that they are motivated to change.

It also gives them a little time to reflect on what is often a very confused aspect of their life. Surprisingly, many clients have not thought about their eating disorder in this way before. For them, it is often one big complicated mystery. The questionnaire lets them consider different parts of their eating disorder separately and remove some of the emotion from the experience.

So, your first step to recovery is to fill in this short questionnaire. You might be surprised about what these questions tell you about yourself.

PRE-MEETING QUESTIONNAIRE

This simple questionnaire, just five questions, gives a great deal of insight into the extent of the problem and what causes the most pain. The answers are very revealing.

Take a moment to fill in the questionnaire. This is not an exam! It doesn't matter how much or how little information you put in there. What is important is that you think truthfully about your answers. Once you've finished, read on to see what you can learn about yourself.

This one's for you

1. When did food first become a problem for you?	
2. What does a good day look like?	
3. What does a bad day look like?	
4. If you could change one thing, what would it be?	
5. What was the 'last straw' that made you look for help?	

Have a quick look at what you have written. Have you learned anything? Did anything surprise you? If so, write it down.

HOW TO ANALYSE YOUR PRE-MEETING QUESTIONNAIRE

To help you to understand what your pre-meeting questionnaire tells you, I will go through each question and give you the reason why I ask each question and the insights that I get from each answer. But, more importantly, I will point out what insights you might get from what you have written.

When did food first become a problem to you?

WHY I ASK THIS QUESTION

This gives an overview of your eating disorder. It gives an idea of what the problem is, how long food has been a problem for you and how deeply the problem is established.

WHAT DID YOU LEARN?

- Were you surprised at how long food has been an issue?
- Was there a particular moment when things changed?
- How did you feel about yourself when food first became a problem for you?
- Looking back from now to when food first became a problem for you, how does the present day self see your young self?
- How do you feel now when you think of yourself back then?
- Did it tell you anything else?

What does a good day look like?

WHY I ASK THIS QUESTION

I ask this question for two reasons: Firstly, to get an understanding of what you think of as a 'good day'; does it seem reasonable or have you set the bar very high for what counts as a 'good day'? Secondly, many people tend to count the bad things and not remember the good things that they have achieved. This forces them to remember that they do have 'good days'.

WHAT DID YOU LEARN?

• Is there a pattern to a 'good day'?
• What were you doing on a 'good day'?
• How were you handling life's problems on a 'good day'?
• How would you like this to be your 'every day' experience? That's sometimes not so easy to answer.

What does a bad day look like?

WHY I ASK THIS QUESTION

I ask this question to get an insight of the true awfulness of the situation, the extent of the power the eating disorder has over your quality of life.

If the answers to question 2 are characterised by the word 'calm', the answers to question 3 are usually characterised by the word 'chaos'. This helps you understand the true extent of the disorder and it gives an indication of the areas that will need addressing.

WHAT DID YOU LEARN?

• Is there a pattern to a 'bad day'?
• What do you feel when you read your words?
• Do you feel sorry for the person suffering in these words?
• How does s/he feel? What is s/he thinking?
• Think about how you wish you could help her/him – what would you tell her/him?

If you could change one thing what would that be?

WHY I ASK THIS QUESTION

This highlights the 'pain point' – the key aspect of the eating disorder which is causing the most anguish. This is the area I try to address first, because the client is highly motivated to end this pain and, once we have succeeded in such a painful area, it builds confidence to tackle other areas.

WHAT DID YOU LEARN?

You have put into words the thing about your eating disorder that is causing you the most pain. This knowledge is a key lever on your road to recovery. It will be key to maintaining your motivation over the period of your recovery and is especially important in the early stages. When your disorder fights back (and it will fight back), you need to keep this point to the front and centre of your mind. This is your key motivation to change. This is the pain that will happen again and again if you listen to your eating disorder. Every time you waver on your journey into recovery, remember this pain – you don't want to go back there.

What was the 'last straw' that made you ask for help?

WHY I ASK THIS QUESTION

The 'last straw' moment is the key pain point, the thing that happened that caused you to say, 'That's enough – I need help.' The vast majority of my clients usually write something along the lines of 'I'm just tired of carrying on like this.' They might be embarrassed to reveal the real reason to me, a stranger. But they know what the last straw was deep inside and this question makes them remember how they felt when it happened. This is a key moment which will motivate you throughout your recovery.

WHAT DID YOU LEARN?

Whether you wrote it down or not, simply thinking about that 'last straw' moment crystalizes in your mind what will happen over and over again unless you change. And it's the thought of living the rest of your life like that has prompted you to look for help. You don't need me to tell you that this is an act of courage.

EXAMPLES TO PRACTICE ON

Here are two examples to help you analyse your pre-meeting questionnaire. They are based on two real-life clients of mine. If you look closely, you will see that both Jane and Susan have identified what started their eating disorder and their answers give them a good idea of how to solve their problem. But Jane and Susan just cannot see it. They are intelligent people but firstly, they are too close to their problem and secondly, what the forms clearly show is diametrically opposite to what our culture and its obsession with thinness tells them.

EXAMPLE 1: JANE

1. When did food first become a problem for you?	I had a problem with bulimia from my late twenties. I started a diet after a very stressful period in my life which led to very extreme dieting and exercise and then developed into bulimia. I've now got the purging under control since having children but struggle with binge eating instead.
2. What does a good day look like?	Eating three sensible meals and exercise and feeling positive.
3. What does a bad day look like?	Erratic eating followed by a binge and guilt and depression.
4. If you could change one thing, what would it be?	I would like to have a normal appetite and some control around food.
5. What was the 'last straw' that made you look for help?	I have done counselling in the past, but I have put on a lot of weight recently and this is affecting my family life and relationships.

I wonder what you would advise Jane to do. I know that it might be becoming obvious to you, but Jane is far too close to her situation and completely blind to what is causing the problem and the answer.

When I read Jane's responses, I was struck that Jane knew what started her eating disorder: *'very extreme dieting and exercise and then developed into bulimia.'*

She knew what made it worse: *'erratic eating followed by a binge and guilt and depression.'*

And she knew how to stop the bingeing: *'eating three sensible meals and exercise and feeling positive.'*

Just from reading this short pre-meeting questionnaire, what would you advise Jane to do?

This one's for you

I would suggest doing more of the thing she did on a good day and avoiding/less of what she did on a bad day. Sounds simple, right?

EXAMPLE 2: SUSAN

1. When did food first become a problem for you?	I've always had a weight issue. But I think, in reality, it's become a problem over the last year or two. I seem to be swinging between extreme dieting and eating everything I can.
2. What does a good day look like?	I feel happy and positive. I don't feel hungry and I am in control. I don't have the desire to eat rubbish.
3. What does a bad day look like?	I feel down, depressed and deprived. I don't drink or smoke and see food as my only vice, even if it means doing it secretly as I feel ashamed.
4. If you could change one thing, what would it be?	My eating habits.
5. What was the 'last straw' that made you look for help?	My problem has become out of control and it's affecting my marriage and my life and my happiness.

In this case, Susan has pinpointed the cause of her distress: *'I seem to be swinging between extreme dieting and eating everything I can.'*

She tells us what if feels like on a bad day, but doesn't say how she is eating. However, the fact that she justifies what she is doing – *'food is my only vice'* – and she is doing it in secret, is a hint that she is probably bingeing.

From reading her answers, what would you advise Susan to do?

This one's for you

I would suggest finding out exactly what she is doing on a good day. Does she meet with friends, change the structure of her day, get up earlier? If it is not extreme dieting – do it more often.

Do you want to revise your thoughts on your own answers from what you've learned from Jane and Susan?

When I first meet my clients, we discuss the pre-meeting questionnaire and what they learned from filling it out. For many, this is the first time they have admitted to anyone, including themselves, the length and extent of their condition, and they find the act of filling in the questionnaire quite cathartic and experience a release of emotions.

WHAT I HAVE LEARNT FROM MY ANSWERS

BITESIZE

You have looked in detail at your pre-meeting questionnaire and see what it tells you about your problem with eating. Go back to your completed questionnaire and consider your answers, using my explanation of 'why I ask the questions' as a guide.

- You will now be able to identify how long food has been a problem and what kicked off your eating disorder.

- You will be able to identify the positive feelings you can feel around food when things are going well.

- You will definitely know just how bad things can get.

- You will have identified what is the worst part of your eating disorder for you – your 'pain point'

- Finally, you will have identified the 'last straw' moment when you thought 'I can't do this anymore and need help'.

This knowledge will help you to maintain your motivation throughout your recovery programme.

MY NOTES

This one's for you

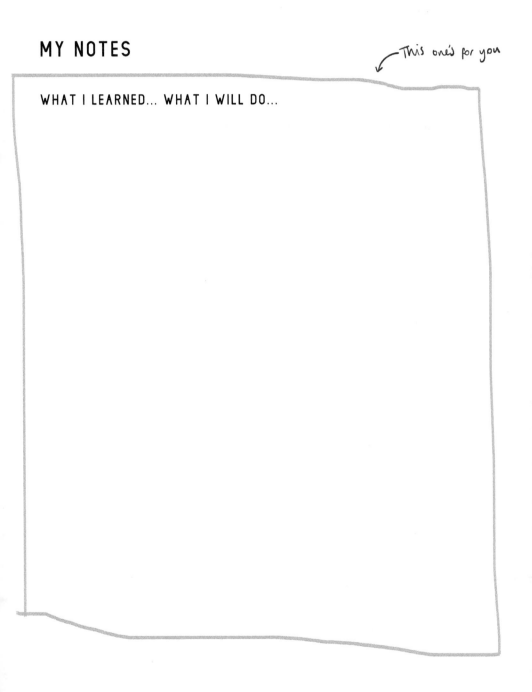

WHAT I LEARNED... WHAT I WILL DO...

CHAPTER THREE

THE THINGS THAT KEEP AN EATING DISORDER FIRMLY IN PLACE

Your answers to the questionnaire in the previous chapter have helped you understand the extent to which your eating disorder is affecting your life. Let's now look at some of the things that keep it firmly in place.

My next question to you is: 'Why do you think you binge?'

For most people, it is quite a mystery, but they have a good understanding of what leads up to a bingeing session:

"I'm very good at controlling what I eat during the day, but somehow at night I find myself bingeing" Raul

"It's as if somebody else takes over and although I keep telling myself, 'I will not binge today', I seem to watch myself going from shop to shop to buy binge food for when I get home, almost against my will" Jane

"I'm doing well controlling my food and I can hear the cheesecake singing to me from the fridge" Susan

"No matter how hard I try to fight it, a voice in my head seems to say, "Why fight it? You know you are going to have to binge, no matter how hard you try." Jean

"Some days I'm fine, I go to the gym and I'm in control, and other times I'm bingeing all day and purging over 10 times a day. It's costing me a fortune, but I can't stop" Chris

Does this or some variation of it sound familiar? You are happily in control when suddenly, something happens, and you find yourself compelled to binge. Feeling that something outside your control is making you do things that you don't want to do is bad enough. But with it comes a shadow meaning: nobody else seems to act in this way so – 'there must be something wrong with me.'

How bad must it be to think that, deep down, there is something basically wrong with you and not knowing what it is or how to put it right? Well, let's put that one to bed right now. There is nothing wrong with you – it is just that at some point in your life you have made a wrong turn and ended up here. Anybody who does what you do, with the same amount of determination, will end up where you are.

The reason it is such a mystery is that an eating disorder is complicated and made up of many parts, and each of these parts have an effect on the rest. You are trying to hit a moving target. Changes to one part will have a knock-on effect on the other parts of the disorder.

The best way to think of an eating disorder is as an energy system, like a whirlwind surrounding a person.

AN EATING DISORDER IS AN ENERGY SYSTEM, LIKE A WHIRLWIND SURROUNDING A PERSON [1]

Like a whirlwind, an eating disorder sucks energy from many different parts of the body and mind and whips it up into a storm around the person in the centre – YOU. Eating disorders thrive on instability and anxiety – the more instable a person feels, the stronger the eating disorder becomes. The energy is sucked from different parts and builds into a raging storm around the person.

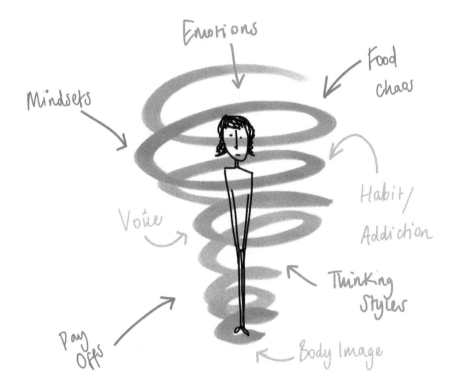

This makes it very difficult for the person wrapped up in the storm to see what is causing the problem, let alone do anything about it. Worse still, attempts to change one of these factors tends to provoke anxiety in the other factors, which increase the instability and strength of the disorder. For example, eating better reduces the physical stress but increases anxiety around getting fat.

Don't worry though, you will learn how to stabilise each of these elements and, with stability, your eating disorder, like a whirlwind, will lose momentum and fade away.

1 This is a metaphor was taught to me by Deanne Jade, Founder and Principal of the National Centre for Eating Disorders – thanks Deanne

ENERGY SOURCES OF AN EATING DISORDER

Let's have a look at the different energy sources that may be contributing to your eating disorder.

Food Chaos:

Cycles of bingeing and restriction lead to instability in the form of **Food Chaos**. This wreaks havoc on the body, mind and emotions. The instability of food chaos both weakens the sufferer, while at the same time strengthens the disorder. Over time, this dynamic makes the person feel helpless. Does this sound familiar?

We will remove the negative energy and stabilise your body using nutrition rehabilitation. This is not another diet sheet or set of rules. It involves learning:

- to stabilise your blood sugar,
- hunger skills,
- craving skills, and
- will-power skills.

Habit:

Simple habit plays a major role and for some there is an element of addiction. We will remove the energy from this area by re-wiring that part of the brain with new, more positive habits so you can use this 'saved' energy to do something more fun.

Payoffs:

Everybody gets some payoffs from their eating disorder. These can seem positive in the short term, but they often make matters much worse. When I ask my clients, 'What do you get from bingeing?', they often say that they feel helpless, guilty, angry or ashamed.

I then say, 'No, that's later. What do you feel during or just after a binge?'

Then the real payoffs come out. For some, it's the only way they can have fun or eat the food they yearn. For others, it's a massive release of stress or being able to eat what they want without feeling guilty. Whatever it is, it is important to recognise that in some way bingeing is useful to you. There are costs to pay later, but in the moment, it feels great. I know it seems a strange source of energy for your eating disorder, but it is not. For example, say you are doing well and putting in place positive change. You might start to wonder, if something bad happens in the future, 'How am I going to cope?' And this provokes anxiety thinking about all the bad things that could happen if you no longer had bingeing to help you cope. This anxiety can contribute to the energy that keeps you firmly stuck.

Ask yourself what your payoffs are from bingeing. Write them down:

This one's for you

When you wrote that down, did you feel a little sad or even scared inside? Did you think:

'Oh no, if I don't binge I won't be able to get that payoff anymore!'

It's almost like losing a friend. It's not, but the problem is thinking like this will put you in two minds about change and this can undermine your recovery. Don't worry, you will soon be able to do all the things that you think you will miss (and more) once you have recovered. Recovery is NOT about cutting things out of your life, it's about adding things to your life and expanding your choices so you have the time and energy to do much, much more in your life.

Emotions:

I mentioned earlier that some people are more susceptible to developing an eating disorder than others. Being sensitive with perfectionist tendencies makes you particularly vulnerable to your emotions.

A sensitive person can be hurt badly by a chance remark that other people would hardly notice. Perfectionists are particularly hard on themselves for not being, well, 'perfect'. You can imagine that a person who is easily hurt and constantly berating themselves will sometimes feel overwhelmed by their emotions. At such times, the eating disorder can provide temporary relief by 'zoning out' and dulling down the emotions.

This is a powerful source of energy for the disorder. In the programme, there will be homework that will teach you ways of managing your emotions so that stress and anxiety rarely build up to uncomfortable levels.

Mind Set:

Another large part of the energy system is mind set, a set of general attitudes around the way we think about things. This is what you bring to the therapy and can have a major effect on sustaining good habits and finally recovering from your eating disorder.

Beliefs:	About food, shape and weight.
Food Script:	Good/bad foods, clean your plate, starving children in Africa etc.
Thinking Styles:	Black and white thinking ('I'm good or I'm bad, there are no shades of grey'), catastrophising (something bad happens and you think the worst thing imaginable will probably happen – boss wants a word with you about your work and you immediately imagine getting fired and losing your home) etc. Perhaps you say to yourself, 'I've blown it', after a small deviation from your plan, which changes your behaviour.
Personality:	Feeling either in control or totally out of control.
Body Image:	'What I look like/should look like/how others see me.' Beauty and the beast thinking – she looks beautiful which means I look terrible.
Mind Reading:	Guessing what others are thinking as if it was a fact – 'No one can like me with these thighs.'
Labelling:	Fat/thin/greedy/loser – you get the message.
The Critical Voice in your head:	That poisonous parrot on your shoulder which starts off as your friend but soon becomes a tyrant that haunts your thoughts.
Perfectionist Tendencies:	Always like to be on time, 9 out of 10 is a fail.

Just reading this list gives you an idea of how much energy is being sucked from your life and into your disorder. We only have so much energy – it is draining to use it in such a negative way. As you work through the programme you will find that you will become more gentle and loving to yourself and many of the mind set issues will simply disappear.

THE ELEPHANT IN THE ROOM

Before we go any further, let's address the elephant in the room. Deep down, most people are in two minds about recovery. They often don't like to admit this, even to themselves, but unless we address this head on it has a tendency to undermine recovery attempts at a later stage.

Why would anybody want to keep an eating disorder? It doesn't make sense. Well, there is the sheer exhilaration of gorging yourself without restraint, but more importantly, you are probably getting something much more important to you. We touched on this in 'pay-off' earlier.

- Does it make you feel special in some way?
- Does it give you a feeling of being in control?
- Does it relieve the stress that builds up?
- Have you been doing it so long that it seems you've been wasting all that time if you stop now?

Think about what your eating disorder does for you and I'll bet some part of you feels a little sad at the thought of losing it – how are you going to feel special or in control or relieve stress once you have recovered?

"I'm also scared. As much as I want to beat this, I do really enjoy sitting on the sofa with a large bag of Dairy Milk buttons, some Kettle Chips and wine gums ... the thought of losing this 'friend' is very daunting." Gilly

THE 'NEW NORMAL'

Amy Johnson used the idea of the 'new normal' to help her recover from years of binge eating. In her book, 'The little book of big change', she explains the importance of understanding the 'new normal' by using the example of how she finally stopped smoking.

After several failed attempts, Amy looked at what she was gaining by continuing to smoke, what the pay off was for her. She realised that after a stressful day at work she would sit down, smoke a cigarette and relax. At some level, she thought that if she gave up smoking she would not be able to relax after work. This put her in two minds about quitting smoking, and every time she tried she would self-sabotage her quit attempt.

What Amy learned was that going into nicotine withdrawal increased her stress levels. The relief she felt from having a cigarette reduced this artificial rise in her stress levels.

Amy realised that a great deal of the stress she was relieving by smoking was caused by smoking and, once she quit smoking, the stress naturally disappeared. In effect, she had a 'new normal' where she no longer needed to find a way to relax, because she was relaxed.

You will find that once you recover you will no longer need what your eating disorder is giving you. You will have a 'new normal' where you:

- won't have to feel special, you will know you are special.
- will not need to feel in control and that's fine.
- will not need to relieve the stress because it doesn't build up.

"Now if I want, I can still enjoy sitting on the sofa with a bag of Dairy Milk buttons, some Kettle Chips and wine gums. But somehow, I don't seem to want anymore. If I do have some chocolates or crisps, now I can enjoy them without the guilt and shame." – Gilly

There is nothing wrong with you. Anyone who does what you do will finish up in the same place.

- An eating disorder is a complex condition and draws energy from many different physical and psychological parts of you.

- Reducing one source of energy in one part tends to increase instability in other sources of energy.

- By cutting off these sources of energy, one by one the eating disorder will have no energy to maintain itself and simply fade away.

- You need expert knowledge to work your way back to being normal around food.

This book will give you the knowledge you need and the skills and techniques to recover.

MY NOTES

This one's for you

WHAT I LEARNED... WHAT I WILL DO...

NOW, WITH THAT IN MIND, LET'S GET ON WITH THE PROGRAMME.

CHAPTER FOUR

FOOD KNOWLEDGE

First of all, I would like to say well done for looking for help.

You now know how the eating disorder is kept firmly in place by drawing energy from many different parts of your life. You have filled in your pre-meeting questionnaire and have a good understanding of what it tells you about you and your relationship with food. You are raring to go, but with so many complicated, interrelated physical, psychological and emotional areas involved, where do you start?

FOOD CHAOS

We always start by getting the food chaos under control by stabilising the blood sugar levels. Food chaos arises when someone is in a constant cycle of either restricting what they eat by dieting or they are bingeing. This causes wild fluctuations in blood sugar levels.

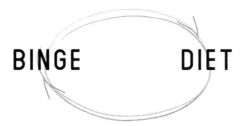

BINGE   **DIET**

These fluctuations cause a great deal of stress to both mind and body and, as you know from the previous chapter, they are a major energy source for your eating disorder.

Unstable blood sugar levels, amongst other things, explain:

- why cravings happen.
- why weight is gained rapidly.
- why you can overeat, even when full.

You might not realise it, but you have felt the power of unstable blood sugar and how it affects how you feel: physically, psychologically and emotionally.

Think back to how you feel just before a binge. You may have been doing really 'well', cutting back your food and exercising and you are feeling very pleased with yourself. Sounds great, but what you are doing is ignoring your internal hunger cues. The problem is that hunger puts your body under unmanageable stress which, because you are ignoring your hunger cues, you are not aware of consciously. But your body is aware and floods your system with stress hormones. Then, out of the blue, you feel a bit anxious and the anxiety starts to build and build. You keep thinking about bingeing while at the same time trying to resist the urge to binge. It's almost like you have a devil on one shoulder saying, 'Go on, binge, you know you will in the end,' and an angel on the other shoulder saying, 'No, you are not weak, you will not binge'. The problem is that internal arguments like this only increase the tension and anxiety until the inevitable happens.

Stage one: I've blown it.

You try just one or two biscuits – 'That won't hurt, will it!' – and, before you know it, you have eaten half a packet of biscuits and you feel that you've 'blown it', so you might as well eat the whole packet.

Stage two: The Last Supper.

'Don't worry,' you tell yourself, you will get back on track the next day and cut back on your eating and do a little more exercising to make up for the packet of biscuits. Which nicely sets you up for stage two, 'The Last Supper' syndrome. You realise that you will have to really cut back the next day, no more treats, so you might as well eat as much as you can while you can, so you hunt around the house for any treats you can find, because you will have to really deprive yourself of them the next day.

Stage three: Better eat everything in the house.

You start to worry that you may be tempted to overeat the next day, so you had better get rid of all temptation from the house, so you eat everything you can find.

Stage four: Zoned out.

When you can't eat anything else and the food kicks in, you find the anxiety has gone and you feel so relaxed and zoned out from all your problems, without a care in the world, happy and safe in the knowledge that you will sort it all out the next day.

Stage five: The fresh start.

You wake up in the morning and realise what you've done. You are wracked with guilt and shame and you resolve to make a fresh start. You eat really well (code for cutting back on food) and hit the gym, setting yourself up for stage one and another round of bingeing.

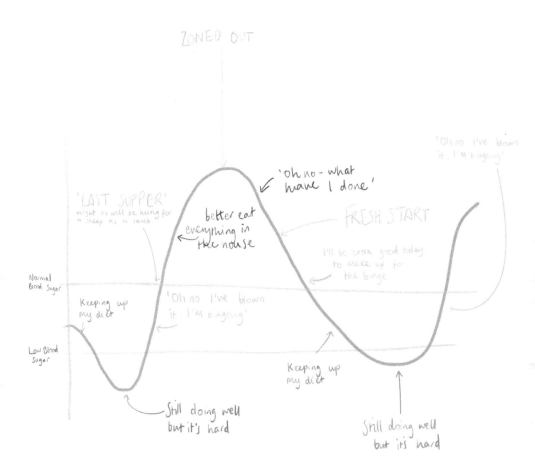

These are the dramatic effects of unstable blood sugar, which I am sure you have experienced many times. You know that once the binge gets underway there is nothing you can do to stop it. The way to stop the effects of food chaos is to stabilise your blood sugar levels.

This is not so difficult, but it does require 'food knowledge', a little planning and some experimenting to find out what works best for you and how you live.

FOOD KNOWLEDGE

If you are like my clients, you probably think you know everything there is to know about food. They know the number of calories and fat content of everything in the supermarket. But most of my clients have little understanding about what happens to the food once it has entered the body. But it is important to have a good understanding of how the body uses food, what it does when there is too much food and, most importantly, what it does when there is not enough food. Understanding what happens to food once it is inside the body will give you the knowledge to work with your body to stabilise the food chaos using nutritional rehabilitation.

NUTRITIONAL REHABILITATION

Nutritional rehabilitation is not just a diet sheet. You will develop hunger skills so that you can become attuned again to your hunger levels, develop skills to deal with cravings and the ability to not only make good decisions around food, but be able to carry them out.

Let's start with the most basic of questions.

We all want to live healthily, so how much food does your body need to function healthily? How many calories do you think you need to eat a day to be healthy?

This seemingly innocuous question often leaves a stunned silence from my clients and eventually they might mention something along the lines of:

'It's supposed to be about 2,000 for a woman – isn't it?'

It's obvious that they have heard this number somewhere, but it's an abstract number that has no real relevance to them. So, I push them a little, and make it concrete.

'So 2,000 calories – what would you have to eat in a day to get 2,000 calories? I mean, a breakfast of say 2 rashers of bacon, tomatoes and 2 slices of toast would be about 350 calories. A lunch of a jacket potato, half a tin of beans & cheese, that's about another 400 calories, and for supper, lets push the boat out with 1lb (400 gram) piece of lasagne ready meal, salad and a nice piece of crusty bread – about 650 calories.'

I usually stop at this point and let them think about it. So, take a moment and let that sink in.

This one's for you

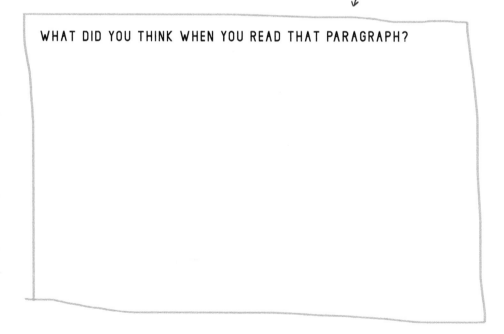

WHAT DID YOU THINK WHEN YOU READ THAT PARAGRAPH?

Most of my clients can only dream of eating such food, let alone in these amounts. The quantities seem huge, but it is the thought of someone suggesting eating bacon, cheese and even lasagne, foods that many have forbidden themselves for so long, is just jaw-droppingly unreal.

Now for the fun.

'So 350 calories for breakfast, 400 for lunch and a whopping 650 calories for supper: that only adds up to 1400 calories. That's almost starvation level. You still need another 600 calories to be healthy. You'd need at least 3 good snacks between meals.'

This provokes disbelief. What do you think when you read this? None of my clients can imagine eating food like this and having to snack as well just to be healthy. Many have been eating far fewer calories for years and thinking they are actually overeating. But the fact is, if you need 2000 calories a day to be healthy (and you may need much more), you need 2000 calories to be healthy. Chronic under-eating is not healthy and can be very damaging to your health.

LET'S GET PERSONAL

Let's make this more concrete and ask the question:

How many calories do YOU need to be healthy?

There are online tools which help you to calculate the minimum amount of calories you need to be healthy.

First, pick a reputable website (not one selling slimming aids etc.).
I recommend the United States Department of Agriculture (USDA) Dietary Reference Calculator (DRI) for Health Care Professionals.

I will walk you through the process by filling in the details of a 35-year-old woman who is 5 feet 5 inches tall (165cm) and weighs 10 stone (140lbs or 64kgs), with a low activity level. Here are the results

GENDER	FEMALE
AGE	35
HEIGHT	5FT 5 (165CM)
WEIGHT	10 STONE (140LB 64KG)
ACTIVITY LEVEL	LOW ACTIVITY
BMI	23.4
DAILY NEEDS	2121 KCALS

So, we can see this woman has a BMI of 23.4, bang in the middle of the so-called 'healthy BMI' (sic) and, with a low level of activity, needs 2121 calories a day to be healthy.

Now you know what a woman weighing 10 stone (140lbs) should be eating, do the maths (or better still, use the calculator) to find out what you would have to eat in order to be healthy.

Plus, it's worth noting that she needs 2121 calories of nourishing food as part of a well-balanced diet. If you eat a lot of junk food, you might eat the calories but still not get the nutrition your body needs.

Write down here how many calories you need to be healthy

I know this can seem a lot of calories compared to what you are eating, but is it? Compared to what you eat on the days when you are dieting hard, it might seem like a lot. But once you add in the calories that you eat when you binge, it might be less than you are eating now. I know this is a stark difference to what you have been led to believe for many years, but just take a deep breath and go with it. You will soon feel the benefit of this new knowledge.

Now you know how much good quality food you need every day to be healthy. Did the figure surprise you? I'll bet it was far higher than you thought.

What was the first thing that jumped into your mind?

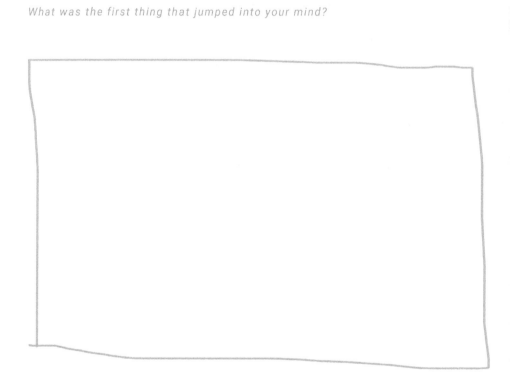

If, like the majority of my clients, you are eating fewer calories than you need, it's tempting to say, 'I'm eating less than I need. I must be losing weight. YEAH!'

Just think about that for a moment… You are eating less than your body needs to function healthily… and somehow that's a good thing? Really?

You might think that it must be good, so that you can lose weight

But, probably like my clients, you're not losing weight. In fact, you might be steadily gaining weight. So, why is that happening?

Perhaps you think that the Estimated Daily Calorific Needs calculation is wrong for you? Unfortunately, it's not the calculation that's wrong, but your understanding (and to be fair, most people's understanding) of weight loss that is wrong. This is why you need to have good food knowledge.

FOOD KNOWLEDGE – THE CALORIES-IN, CALORIES-OUT MYTH

Before we go any further, we need to, once and for all, put to bed one of the biggest myths that has ever taken hold in western society – the calories-in, calories-out myth.

Most people think that to lose weight is a simple matter of calories in and calories out. If you eat more calories than you use you will put weight on, and if you eat less calories than you use you will lose weight – simple.

Simple, yes – but very, very, wrong. Never has such a blunder of simplistic thinking taken hold for so long and caused such untold suffering, both mental and physical, as this misrepresentation of the facts.

'But it's science so it must be right'

It's science, you might argue. The laws of thermodynamics clearly state that energy can neither be created nor destroyed, only changed. So, if we eat less, the body needs to get the energy from somewhere, so it uses up the energy that it has stored as fat. And we get slimmer – it's obvious.

If it was that simple, diets would work, and we would all be slim. Clearly, that is not the case so what is happening?

The problem is that although the laws of thermodynamics apply to physics in a simple cause and effect way, when it comes to the human body, they still apply but in a far more complex way.

THE BODY HAS CHOICES

There is nothing in the laws of thermodynamics that suggest that if the body does not have enough calories to function properly, it has to burn fat. The body has many ways of reacting to fewer calories than simply to burn fat. In fact, burning fat is one of the last things the body does. It's important to understand that the body has choices and it makes them according to its priorities – to survive. It has systems and processes developed over hundreds of thousands of years of evolution to keep you alive. What you want is not even on its agenda. It will perceive undereating as a threat to survival and will put powerful processes in place to ensure that you will survive as long as possible. You might want to lose some weight, but this is irrelevant to your body, as it is concerned with keeping you alive.

To explain why the calories-in, calories-out theory is a myth when applied to the body, let's get all philosophical and have a thought experiment.

What would you do if you were suddenly made redundant? You would probably go home and talk to your spouse, family or friends and weigh up the options. The family wage (which was enabling you to just manage) has halved. But you have enough money in the bank to last three months. So, what do you do?

Do you carry on as usual, supplement your loss of earnings with the money in the bank and hope to get another job before your saving runs out? Well, you could do that but it's a bit risky. What if you don't get another job in time? What would happen then?

It is much more likely that you would cut back on your spending: cancel the holiday, cut back on the food shopping, stop buying clothes, stop eating out, switch the heating down as low as possible, stop all subscriptions to the gym, Netflix, etc. If you cut out all the luxuries, you might be able to survive until you get a job. It's not much fun, but hey, you're surviving.

That money in the bank now becomes so much more valuable to you. It represents survival, not just a bit extra for luxuries. Spending a penny from your savings is like pulling teeth.

You concentrate all your waking hours on looking for a new job, feeling more and more anxious with every day that passes.

Three months later you finally get a job – YEAH! What do you do? Do you go back to spending how you were before you lost your job? Maybe... More realistically, you've got used to living at this lower level. This is your new baseline, a new normal. You'll gradually add some of the cheaper luxuries and put the rest in the bank for a rainy day. After the shock of the last three months you want to be better prepared next time, and each month you will save more money, building your bank balance against future hard times.

But lightning strikes twice. Three months into the new job you are suddenly made redundant again, so what do you do? You go home again to talk to your spouse, family or friends and weigh up the options.

The family wage has once again been halved. But now you have a new baseline for normal and have saved enough money in the bank to last five months.

So, do you carry on as usual, supplementing your loss of earnings with the money in the bank and hope to get another job before the savings runs out? This seems more reasonable, because you have lower outgoings and more money in the bank.

Well, you could do that but it's still a bit risky. What if you don't get another job in time? Plus, you have another concrete example of how unreliable jobs are even if you are lucky enough to get one. That little bit of money is all that is keeping the wolf from the door and becomes even more valuable to you.

So instead, most likely you cut back. But after a few of these cycles, it gets harder and harder because eventually you will have already cut back on the luxuries and there are no more 'nice to have' things left to cut.

It's time to look at the 'need to have' things. You would look at the things that cost you the most, like your car, and sell them. You stop things like your insurance policies, and take a chance that you will be ok.

It's not living but you are surviving. Yes, you feel anxious all the time wondering how you are going to cope and spend every waking hour either looking for a job or worrying about what will happen if you don't get one. But at least you are keeping the money in the bank for a rainy day.

When you have a reduction in your earnings, you have many more options than frittering away the money in the bank. Similarly, when you eat less than you need, your body has many more options open to it than simply burning fat.

HOW YOUR BODY REACTS WHEN YOU DON'T EAT ENOUGH FOOD.

Let's compare the example of how you react to losing your job with how your body reacts to a sudden reduction of food, such as when you go on a restrictive diet, cutting back on calories from 2,000 a day to 1,000 a day. Eating 1,000 calories a day less than you need is quite common practice and I'm sure quite a lot of you are eating even less. In the trade, we call this a deficit of 1,000 calories.

That 1,000 calories a day will give a deficit of 7,000 calories a week. Coincidently, 1 pound of fat is generally considered around 3,500 calories, so a deficit of 7,000 calories should mean that you will lose 2 pounds of fat a week. Two pounds a week equals 8 pounds a month – wow, that's over 3½ stones or 48 pounds in 6 months! All you need is a little will power and you will have your beach body ready for the holidays.

Hmmm, funny that, isn't it? It never seems to happen.

CALORIES IN, CALORIES OUT MYTH

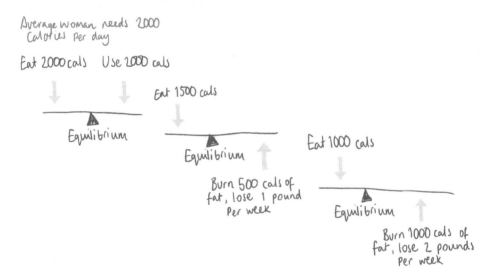

Average woman needs 2000 Calories per day

Eat 2000 cals   Use 2000 cals

Equilibrium

Eat 1500 cals

Equilibrium

Burn 500 cals of fat, lose 1 pound per week

Eat 1000 cals

Equilibrium

Burn 1000 cals of fat, lose 2 pounds per week

Well, to put it simply, it's because the body reacts in the same way as someone would when faced with reduced income after losing their job. It keeps hold of the fat (like savings in the bank) and cuts back on things that use a lot of energy, like keeping the body at a comfortable temperature (you start to feel the cold more). When you feel cold, you put on an extra sweater and the sweater keeps you warm rather than your body burning energy to keep you warm. Your body also lowers your energy levels (you become listless and tired all the time, maybe sleeping more), using less and less of your valuable energy.

HOMEOSTASIS

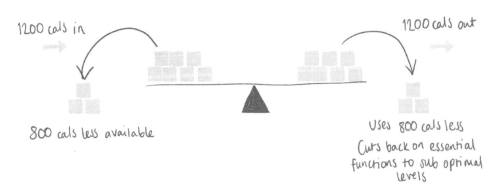

The body reduces energy out to match energy in

1200 cals in

1200 cals out

800 cals less available

Uses 800 cals less
Cuts back on essential functions to sub optimal levels

All this is bad enough, but when the body is not fed enough protein, it does not have the building blocks (amino acids) for essential processes such as producing hormones and repairing damage to the body. When this happens it turns your body into a larder and catabolises your lean muscle. It literally uses your lean muscle as a protein store and breaks down the muscles into the amino acids it needs. Muscles use a lot of energy compared to fat, so by reducing your muscle mass, your body reduces the energy it needs to survive, making weight loss much harder.

At the same time, the brain is alerted that you need food and need it quickly. Suddenly, food is all you can think about; it seems to be everywhere, and you begin to feel deprived. All around you, you see thin people eating what they want and you are starving. Cutting back on calories also results in a lack of the calming brain chemicals (neurotransmitters). This makes you become jumpy, unable to concentrate, impulsive and miserable.

Until one day you fall off the wagon, and in that moment you feel great. Once you start eating you can't seem to stop. Before you know it, you have put the weight back on and you don't feel great anymore. But here's the problem: a lot of the weight you lost was muscle and the weight you put on is almost all fat.

So, each time you cycle through a period of weight loss followed by weight regain you increase your fat to muscle ratio. Your body fat becomes a greater percentage of your body. And fat burns considerably less calories than muscle. This has the effect of reducing your resting metabolic rate (RMR), reducing the amount of energy your body needs to survive.

But all you see is the weight piling on. Panic sets in, something has to be done. So you repeat the cycle again and again, each time the body makes up the deficit by cutting back on essential processes: sex hormones are reduced, and the auto-immune system is compromised.

This is why, as your body reacts to less food, you feel cold all the time, catch every bug that is around, feel worthless, can't concentrate and it feels as though your libido has fallen off a cliff. Oh, and it's all your fault for not having enough willpower! How good does that make you feel?

In this instance, would you say to yourself, 'Hmmm, I'm eating less than I need but I don't seem to be losing weight; restrictive dieting doesn't work, I'll try something else.'

Well, you may say that, but I'll bet it's more likely to be something like, 'I was doing so well, I was eating hardly anything and then I fell off the wagon and had a binge – which ruined all of my hard work. I'll diet and exercise even harder tomorrow and soon get back on track. If I wasn't so weak and had more discipline, I could crack this. I'll get really motivated and stick to it this time.'

And round and round you go, ratcheting your metabolism down and down and blaming yourself.

With every dieting cycle the resting metabolic rate gets pushed further and further downwards until you are existing on a small amount of calories, while at the same time hanging on to your fat.

YO-YO DIETING EXPERIMENT

Kelly Brownell devised a 'Yo-yo Dieting Experiment' where he took a group of rats and put them on a diet. He observed how long it took them to lose weight. Then he allowed them access to unlimited food and observed how long it took for them to put the weight back on. He then repeated the cycle with the same rats.

- **ON THE FIRST ROUND OF DIETING IT TOOK THE RATS 21 DAYS TO LOSE THE WEIGHT AND 45 DAYS TO REGAIN THE WEIGHT.**

- **ON THE SECOND ROUND OF DIETING IT TOOK THE RATS 46 DAYS TO LOSE WEIGHT AND 14 DAYS TO REGAIN IT.**

On the second round, it took **twice as long to lose the weight** and **less than one third of the time to regain the weight.**

In other words, if you under-eat over a period of time, your body will compensate by slowing down your metabolism. It can get so bad that some yo-yo dieters can eat 1000 calories less than they need to be healthy and still not lose weight.

HOMEOSTASIS

The body reduces energy out to match energy in

1000 cals in

1000 cals out

1000 cals less available

Uses 1000 cals less

Stops some essential functions and cuts back on others even more

'That's me, that is. Two years ago I just wanted to lose a few pounds and just look at me now!' Lucy

At the same time, you will become hypervigilant around food, your hunger will increase, or your mind will become obsessed with thoughts of food.

WHAT YOU FOCUS ON GROWS.

All of which increase the chance of bingeing; and once you start eating, not being able to stop. The body wants to get as much food into you as possible to lay down as much fat as possible, so you can survive this period of scarcity.

Isn't your body fantastic! It is focused on keeping you alive and has many ways to override anything you might think is important (like losing weight) but it decides is a threat to your survival. You might not want it to, but like an annoying parent, it has your welfare in mind. It does what it does for your own good – whether you like it or not.

FOOD KNOWLEDGE – TAKE AWAY POINTS

Let's take a moment to look at the food knowledge we have learned. You need a certain amount of food to be healthy and maintain a stable weight. Also, if you eat less than you need, your body will fight back. It does this in two ways: firstly, your body will find ways to cut back on the energy that it needs by slowing down your metabolism and operating at below optimum level; secondly, by making you think about food the whole of the time and intensifying your cravings and reducing your impulse control, it will encourage you to binge.

In other words, dieting (restriction) causes cravings and increases your risk of bingeing, while at the same time making weight loss much more difficult.

Clearly, more dieting, far from being a solution, only makes things worse and can quickly escalate into a vicious cycle of increasing desperation.

BREAKING THE VICIOUS CYCLE

The knowledge that dieting causes bingeing can seem very scary and you may still have trouble believing it is true. Many of my clients have spent years feeling that they are either, 'in control' on a diet, or 'out of control' bingeing. To them, the alternative to dieting seems to be eating out of control, so they are at a loss about what to do. In fact, there is one way which will not only give you quick results but will also build the foundation for your recovery – Stabilising Blood Sugar Levels.

STABILISING BLOOD SUGAR LEVELS

A word of warning: we need to get a bit scientific here, but I think it is important you understand this section fully as it will help you with your recovery. I will make it as simple as possible.

Stabilising Blood Sugar Levels has the effect of stabilising your body with nourishing food whilst, at the same time, rehabilitating your body in a controlled way, kick-starting your metabolism, changing what for many has been years of cycling between bingeing and restricting, reprogramming both your body and your mind. I promise you, if you follow this programme properly, you will feel the results almost immediately. I have seen a complete difference within a week in people who have been dieting and bingeing for decades. After only one week, they are calm, in control and positive, and confident that they can recover.

In order to end food chaos, it is important to understand the effect of stable blood sugar levels on the body, and the consequences of unstable blood sugar levels. This knowledge will allow you to work with your body rather than against it.

THERMOGENIC BODY

When a person who has not been restricting their food eats a balanced meal, the food is digested and the carbohydrates are converted into blood sugar at a steady rate. Blood sugar (or glucose) is the fuel our body needs to work most efficiently – a bit like petrol in a car. When glucose rises in our blood, insulin is released.

EATING A BALANCED MEAL

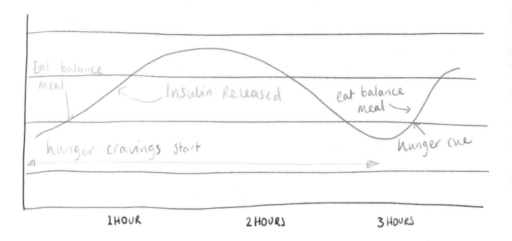

Insulin has three functions that are relevant here:

Firstly, the insulin switches off the fat cells and stops them releasing fatty acids into the blood.

Secondly, the insulin acts as a carrier, allowing the glucose to enter the body's cells. The cells are like little furnaces that convert the glucose into energy and heat. We need this energy to keep us alive because it makes the basic functions of our bodies happen, such as keeping our hearts beating, lungs breathing and allowing us to move about.

This continues for a time and then the blood sugar levels begin to drop at a steady rate. After approximately three hours you will start to feel hungry, so you eat, and the cycle repeats itself. This state is called the thermogenic body, where carbohydrates are changed to blood sugar at a steady rate and the cells have time to convert the blood sugar into energy and heat.

So far, so good.

The problem arises when we eat less than we need and our blood sugar levels drop to a low level. As we have seen, the body fights back and eventually we break down and have a binge. Unfortunately, when a binge happens, it is rarely (if ever) a balanced meal or a broccoli bake. When you binge, you tend to eat large amounts of foods, such as bread, biscuits, ice cream and other sugary fatty foods that are easily digested and rapidly turned into glucose. This causes a rapid increase in the blood sugar levels, which in turn causes a rapid spike in the amount of extra insulin in the blood. The level is too high for the cells to convert all the blood sugar into energy.

Once the blood sugar hits a certain level the brain instructs insulin to enact its third function and rapidly reduce the blood sugar levels by dropping the glucose into fat cells, storing it as fat for future use. The problem is, because of the extra insulin in the blood, this process tends to over-shoot the optimum blood sugar level, causing the body to drop into low blood sugar or extreme hunger. You know how this feels: one minute you are zoned out by all the food you ate and the next minute it's like falling off a cliff and you are starving again. Low blood sugar levels are extremely uncomfortable and it will force you to eat and eat quickly, prompting further rounds of bingeing, resulting in the body getting fatter.

The process following a binge is much quicker, and it only takes about 90 minutes before you are hungry again. Ironically, eating the large amount of food on a binge (the food typically eaten on a binge is processed by the body very quickly) has the effect of causing extreme hunger, spurring on another round of bingeing. This is why we can feel hungry even after eating large quantities of food. In effect, dieting turns your body into a fat-making machine.

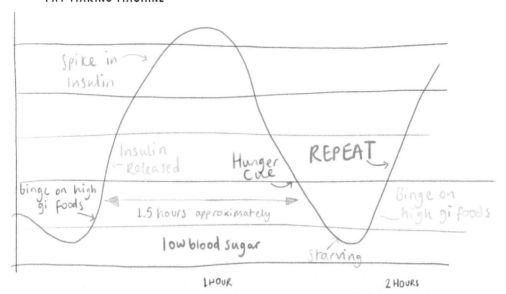

BITESIZE

You now have the basic food knowledge that will let you start working with your body instead of against it. This knowledge will form a firm foundation for your recovery.

You know the following:

- How many calories you need to eat each day to be healthy.

- The body has many choices to deal with undereating.

- That yo-yo dieting makes losing weight more difficult and gaining weight easier.

- The body can convert balanced meals into heat and energy.

- The body tends to convert binges into fat.

The first step in your recovery is to stabilise your blood sugar levels. This will help to change your body from a fat-making machine into a thermogenic body, transforming blood sugar into energy and heat, instead of storing it as fat.

You have a good idea of how the body responds to restriction and what not to do. Now you are in a place to put this knowledge to good use and learn what to do to work with your body and recover. Let's make a start.

MY NOTES

This one's for you

WHAT I LEARNED... WHAT I WILL DO...

SECTION TWO

HOW TO RECOVER FROM YOUR
EATING DISORDER

CHAPTER FIVE

ENDING FOOD CHAOS

The previous chapter outlined the complex way your body reacts to food, but stabilising blood sugar levels is relatively easy. It is achieved by structured eating.

STRUCTURED EATING

Structured eating is a stepping stone to get you from food chaos, where you are now, to eating normally. To being in touch with your internal cues, so that you naturally eat when you are hungry and stop when you are full. Seems like some kind of dream, I know, but it's easily achieved, once you commit to structured eating. Don't worry, it's not another set of rigid rules for you to follow; structured eating is a gentle way of working with your body by:

- regularly feeding your body with the nutritious food it needs.
- stopping eating things that confuse your body.

Structured eating is a flexible guide that sets out how to eat in order to prevent large fluctuations in your blood sugar levels. It is not a long list of do's and don'ts, just a simple framework. This framework will support you in your journey from a place of highly restricted eating full of rules (what to eat, how much, when etc.) to eating normally and paying attention to internal cues of hunger and of being full.

REGULARLY FEEDING YOUR BODY THE NUTRITIOUS FOOD IT NEEDS TO THRIVE

The first step is to eat regularly, and it involves eating approximately every 3 hours throughout the day.

- Eat enough calories to be healthy.
- Eat 3 meals and 3 snacks a day.
- One meal must be a breakfast which contains some carbohydrates – eat within 30 mins of waking. If you find this difficult, have a glass of milk as this is enough to kick start your metabolism.
- Eat plenty of protein.
- Eat food that looks like food. Try not to eat heavily processed food.

The key goal will be to eat regularly throughout the day. We can focus about what you eat later.

I know this can seem scary, because at first it seems like a large amount of food and you feel that your weight is bound to balloon. But bear with me, you might be pleasantly surprised. If in doubt, look back and see how many calories you need to be healthy. You will need to eat 3 meals and 3 snacks to eat enough to be healthy. If you commit to structured eating I can guarantee that you will start feeling much better within a few days.

'I must admit that I was very sceptical at first, when Tony asked me to change to structured eating. I made loads of mistakes in the first week; I didn't stick to it completely, some days I forgot to eat my snack and once I missed my breakfast. But when I saw Tony for our second session, I had to admit that I felt much calmer & in control. Things that would have put me in a spin just didn't seem to matter that much. Funnily, although I had overeaten several times, I did not have a binge that week. This was a big deal for me!

Jo

I don't really care what you eat at first (once you are stable you can always tweak what you eat); eating regularly is the key. If you are unsure what to eat, you should be eating roughly a minimum of:

- 6 portions of starchy food
- 2 portions of protein
- 1 pint of milk (or equivalent)
- 3 portions of fruit and vegetables
- 3 teaspoons of oils and fats

You get to pick what you eat to feed your body with the nutrients it needs. Your body doesn't care where it gets the nutrients, so you might as well eat the food you enjoy – win/win. If you are unsure what to eat, I have put together some Meal Suggestions in Appendix 1.

Now let's look at what to stop doing.

STOP EATING THINGS THAT CONFUSE YOUR BODY

Stop eating things that confuse the body and disrupt your blood sugar levels, such as:

- **Artificial sweeteners** and any products that contain them, such as low calorie or no calorie products. If you want to make something sweeter, try sugar, your body can easily digest sugar.
- **Diet sodas** – If you really want a soda, have a 'full fat' version. Yes, I know they contain a lot of sugar, but at least your body knows how to handle sugar. Plus, you might decide that you don't really need a soda and pick a healthier alternative.
- **Low fat products**, such as, low fat yogurts, low fat desserts, low fat sauce mixes etc. They are usually full of high GI carbohydrates or, more likely, chemicals. These chemicals might help the way this stuff tastes in your mouth, but your body has little or no idea how to process them. Have full fat yoghurts etc. They taste better, don't confuse your digestion, keep you feeling full longer and contain very nourishing nutrients.
- **Trans-fats**, such as margarine or any foods that contain trans-fats, such as low-quality biscuits or pastries. Trans-fat is usually found in highly processed, cheap, ready cooked food. And whether it claims on the packet that it lowers cholesterol or is low fat, avoid them like the plague. Seriously though, why would you eat this stuff when you could be eating butter? Both you and your body will love the change.
- **Products with a long list of additives and preservatives**. Your body is a mammal not a chemistry lab. Give it a break.

Some of you might have already eliminated many or all of the products that confuse the body. If you have, great, you are already ahead of the game. You know how easy it is to live without these products in your life. For others, I know this is a massive step. Especially if you have been using diet drinks as a way of controlling hunger when you were restricting what you ate. You might have been eating low fat/no fat products as a way of giving yourself a guilt-free treat.

You might worry that without these products you will not be able to control your appetite and simply just binge and binge. It's all very well for me to say that this will not happen, but unless you know in your gut that you will be fine, you will not be convinced. Well, the only way to find out is to try it. If you have cereal with skimmed milk and 0% fat yoghurt, try to maybe work up to 2% semi-skimmed milk and natural yoghurt. Trust me, the sooner you are eating real food, the sooner your body will respond and the sooner you will feel the benefits.

When Tony told me to try and cut out diet drinks, I thought "That will never happen." I really love my diet sodas. They are my real treat throughout the day. Tony asked me what I love about them and I said I really love the taste and everything that goes with it. Tony said "If you really love the taste and everything that goes with it, no problem, just have normal soda." I was literally speechless at the thought "But I wouldn't do that!" I said "Yes," Tony said, "but you could. Don't cut out the sodas. Any time you want one, just have a regular soda. I know there's a lot of sugar in them, but your body can handle sugar." I don't know why, but my soda drinking went down day by day. Now if I have a diet soda at my friends house, it tastes horrible compared to the regular soda!   *Sarah*

NOT SURE WHAT TO EAT

Although the structured eating guidelines are relatively simple, many of my clients have been restricting for so long that they have no idea how they are going to manage to eat 3 meals and 3 snacks a day. For some, it is just the practicalities that are a problem, such as 'I can't leave my desk to get a snack,' or, 'I'm driving about a lot and find getting a snack difficult.' If you have similar issues, a little problem solving goes a long way. I remember a junior doctor called Susan, who had recovered from binge eating for several years, but came to see me because she was suddenly getting the urge to binge.

When I'm home at night I can hear the cheesecake singing to me from the fridge.   *Susan*

She filled in her diary (more about the Food and Mood Diary in the next chapter) and was really surprised at how hungry she was getting during the day. I suggested that she should have a snack and she said that it would be impossible to eat during a ward round. We talked about what she could carry in her ward gown that she could eat without being noticed. I told her that when I worked in the NHS, I was always getting called away at meal times and finished up starving. I said that I always carried some dates and I found that if I ate two dates I was good for at least an hour. 'Brilliant,' she said, 'I love dates and can pop one in my mouth without anybody seeing me.' She stopped getting too hungry during the day and the cheesecake stopped singing to her. She still enjoyed the cheesecake, but when she wanted it. The compulsion was gone. The diary gave Susan a real learning experience which she used to her benefit.

Others simply have no idea what to eat. They have been following the strict rules of one diet or another for so long they don't know what to eat for the best. If you are not sure what you can eat, I don't think you can go wrong with starting with the NHS Eatwell Guide which will give you an idea of the portion size of the various types of foods you will need to be healthy. At a more practical level, I have put together some meal suggestions to give you some ideas what to eat for breakfast, lunch and dinner as well as some snack ideas in Appendix 1.

You might be surprised at some of the suggestions in the Meal Suggestions. Many of my clients are astounded that cheese on toast is down as a snack.

Think about your typical day and what you eat. You may have no problem with eating breakfast, or you may say that you just can't eat in the morning. In that case, maybe have a glass of milk or a latte first thing and breakfast a little later. The milk will kickstart your metabolism and you will feel hungry when you eat your breakfast. Always keep snacks with you: in the desk at work, in the car etc. It depends what you like: it could be nuts, a banana or a couple of biscuits, it really doesn't matter. What matters at first is that you eat regularly. Work through your day and, by the end of it, you have a good idea what to eat each day once you start structured eating.

BITESIZE

In the previous section you learned about the effects of food chaos on your mind and body. In this chapter you learned how to put an end to food chaos.

You have the following knowledge:

- How to stabilise your blood sugar levels and end food chaos using Structured Eating.

- How to feed your body regularly with the nutritious food it needs.

- What to stop eating – so you don't confuse your body.

- Some resources to help you feed your body the nutrition it needs.

This one's for you

WHAT I LEARNED... WHAT I WILL DO...

CHAPTER SIX

FOOD AND MOOD DIARY

Time to introduce one of the most powerful tools that will help you on your road to recovery, the Food and Mood Diary. I can almost hear the exasperated sigh that most of you will be making while you think to yourself 'Oh no, not another ******* food diary!' And, in a way you would be correct. Everyone asks you to keep a food diary. However, the reason that most of you have kept a diary in the past has been as an aid to dieting. Having to write down what you eat will help you to eat less. But this food and mood diary is a tool that you can use for a very different reason. The diary is not for me or you to keep a track on how much you're eating. I am asking you to keep one for a much more important reason. This diary will reveal to you what works for your body and what doesn't work for your body. More importantly, it will show you how what you eat influences how you think and feel (both physically and emotionally).

Let me explain: when I outline structured eating to my clients, I watch them nodding along and I can almost hear them saying to themselves, 'Sounds fine, but it won't work for me,' over and over at each point that I introduce. Years ago, I came to the firm conclusion:

"UNTIL YOU FEEL IT
IN YOUR GUT,
YOU WILL NOT REALLY
BELIEVE.
IT'S AT THE LEVEL OF
GOSSIP.

84

By that, I mean all the arguments in the world will not convince somebody of what you are saying until they feel it for themselves. And I mean 'feel'; this is nothing to do with rational thought, it is visceral, you have to feel it in your gut, then you will truly believe.

The Food and Mood Diary is the best way I know of helping you to truly 'feel' the powerful effect that eating has on your body, mind and emotions. We tend to forget how we felt in a particular moment very quickly and the diary will remind you exactly how you felt when you ate your breakfast last Monday or how you felt when you missed your lunch on Wednesday.

In this way, everything that you write will tell you something, whether good or bad. It is all useful. The diary will reveal what really works for you and it will reveal what works against you. If you find you have had a bad day or a good day – have a look at what you have been eating and you will find concrete examples of how what you eat affects you. This way, you can learn more about what makes you tick and how to become happier, more alert and energetic. The idea is to find connections in what you eat and how you feel. You might find some interesting patterns; most people are surprised by how powerful this tool is in their recovery.

But, as I said before, this sounds all so plausible, but you will not really believe it until you feel it in your heart. So, let's try it and see what the Food and Mood Diary reveals about you.

'I was so desperate that I thought "What have I got to lose?" But, after the first week, I thought to myself, "Have I been putting myself through so much misery when all I had to do was eat more and the bingeing would stop?" Well, there was still more work to do, but from that point I knew that I would recover!'

Linda

So, what have you got to lose?

FOOD AND MOOD DIARY

Date								
Time	Food & Drink	Where	Hunger Level	Mood & State of Mind	B	P	Context	Today's Summary

HOW TO FILL IN EACH COLUMN OF THE FOOD AND MOOD DIARY

Time:
Make a note of the time when you eat.

Food and Drink:
Make a note of what you eat.

Where:
Note down where you are when you are eating. For example, you could be in the car, at work, watching tv etc.

Hunger level:
This is the key to re-aligning yourself to inner hunger cues. Mark it from 1 to 5, where 1 is not really hungry and 5 is ravenous. Most of my clients find this

tricky at first. Many no longer get hunger cues and fluctuate from either not being hungry to being ravenous. This is very disconcerting. Once you are at hunger level 5 you are not in a good place to make healthy decisions, you just need to eat and to eat now. Listening to your internal hunger cues will give you advanced warning that you are getting hungry and will need to eat soon.

If this is you, the next time you eat you might think, 'I'm a bit hungry but not ravenous. I'll mark it a 3.' The next time you eat, you might think to yourself, 'I'm a bit hungry but not ravenous, but it's a bit more than a 3, so I'll mark it a 4.' Don't worry about getting it right, but each time you do it you will get better at calibrating your hunger. In a short time you will be able to think to yourself, 'I'm at hunger level 2, I'd better find something to eat in the next 30 minutes when I will be at a 3.' Keep at it and you will soon be in touch with your internal hunger cues.

Mood and state of mind:
State how you are feeling: anxious or impatient or happy etc.

B:
Put a mark in the 'B' column whenever you have a binge. Some people will point out that it should be obvious from what they have eaten. The point here is to note when you feel you have had a binge. As you know there is a world of difference between overeating and bingeing. It is not the amount of food eaten but the feeling of being out of control which is important.

P:
If you vomit or use laxatives, mark in the 'P' column. If you do not purge, please ignore this column.

Context:
This column adds context to what you have written. For example, you might have marked angry in the mood and state of mind column, but if somebody has let you down, it might explain why you were feeling angry.

Today's summary:
At the end of the day, look over your diary and summarise it. This will put the day into some perspective. Many of us focus on the things that went wrong during the day and forget the many things that went right. Summarising the day helps to avoid this tendency and consider what went on in the day as a whole, which is always a good thing.

Annotate your diary:
If you do something well, give yourself a shiny gold star, or a big tick or a smiley face, so that when you look at the page you will know how many good things you did that day without even having to read what you have written.
I know it seems a bit silly, but this little tip really works. I know that eating disorders are no laughing matter, but that doesn't mean you can't have a little fun recovering.

Food is medicine:
The medicine to stabilise your blood sugar is food — so write at the top of each day of the Food and Mood Diary

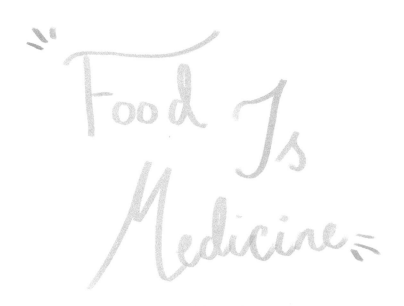

HOW TO USE THE FOOD AND MOOD DIARY

In the past, when you have kept an eating diary, it was probably with the intention of eating less. You know, it would make you think before you eat. Along the lines of 'Do I really want to eat this, because if I do, I'll have to write it in the diary?' or something like, 'If I eat this and write it down, I'll look really greedy.'

But the Food and Mood Diary is not for getting you to eat less, it is a recovery tool. It is a written record of how eating affects your body, thinking and emotional state. For this reason, it is as important to find out what makes things worse (so you can do less of that) as to find out what makes things better (so you can do more of that). What you write is simply data and all data is good, because it tells us something: what to do more of and what to do less of. I tell my clients that the diary is not for me to beat them up with, but it is a tool to show them what works for their body.

When you read your diary, remove any judgement from what you read. A better approach is to have a detached curiosity about what it tells you.

> 'That's interesting. When I had a cappuccino on Monday, I didn't feel hungry for 3 hours, but when I had a cappuccino and a muffin on Wednesday, I was starving after 2 hours. I wonder why?' Karen

There is a physical reason for this, but what would help Karen the most? An abstract understanding about how the body processes food, or her knowing that a cappuccino will hold her for 3 hours, but if she eats a muffin with her cappuccino that she will be starving in 2 hours?

When you have several days logged you can look over the day summaries and think, 'I had a good day on Wednesday, let's have a look at how I ate then,' or, 'I had a terrible day on Monday, let's look at how I ate then.' When you read your diary, look for patterns that lead to consequences – good and bad.

met with a client called Joan. It was 2 weeks since our previous meeting and Joan looked a bit nervous. 'You're going to kill me. I have been terrible this last 2 weeks!' When I asked her to show me her diary, she said that she had not filled it in all week. 'That's a pity,' I said, 'Tell me how you have been getting on.'

It soon emerged that she had had a great deal of stress over a family problem and everything had gone to pot. But as I talked to her, it became apparent that she had handled the family problem really well, plus she:

* stuck to structured eating most of the time
* ate breakfast every day
* had eaten more protein
* stopped drinking diet cola
* hadn't had a binge in over a month

Joan said, 'Well, when you look at it like that, I've not done so bad.'

This is the problem: if you don't keep the diary, you forget how much you have achieved, which is demotivating. Years ago, when I was learning about how to help depressed people, the lecturer said, 'Some people look at the world through rose-coloured spectacles, and others look at the world through shit-coloured spectacles. Who do you think is right?'

We all thought rose-coloured, naturally. He said, 'The world is full of women who stick with abusive husbands and say to themselves, "He'll change," or gamblers who just know "I'll win with this next bet". And that's not good. Others look back on their lives and only notice the bad stuff and to them it all seems terrible. Both coloured glasses are illusions.'

In other words, our thinking style can influence how we see the world. This is normal, but sometimes it can work against us. For example, Joan thought she had been a complete failure the previous two weeks. She had not recognised the great strides she had made, including that for the first time in years she had not binged.

We need a way of testing our impressions of the world with what is actually happening.

The Food and Mood Diary keeps us firmly based in reality. Joan had been looking at the world through shit-coloured glasses and only noticed what went wrong. I said to her, 'Just imagine that you had kept the diary and we could have a look at how you had gone on each day. We would have had concrete example after concrete example of how you had made positive changes day after day. Just imagine how you would feel if you could look at those pages and say, "Yes, I did that and I'm proud of how much I've achieved." How motivated would that make you?'

Joan is fine now. But learn from her example. Keep your Food and Mood Diary and keep yourself firmly grounded in reality.

HOW TO BE MORE FLEXIBLE IN YOUR APPROACH

I know that getting the structured eating in place and keeping the Food and Mood Diary is quite a lot to get your head around. Adequate nutrition is vital, but while you are doing this it is useful to incorporate some exercises to build flexibility into your life at the same time. Many of you will have been dominated by strict rules around food, often for years. Strict rules can seem to reduce anxiety. When you obey, you feel you are doing the right thing. The problem is, they can also cause a lot of anxiety when things don't go to plan. Even when you think that you might break one of the rules you can get anxious.

The Yes /No exercise is a great and fun way of building a little flexibility into your life so that you get used to feeling comfortable without having rules to follow. You can be flexible and do one thing or the other depending on how you feel at that moment.

YES/NO TECHNIQUE

This is a simple exercise where you either:
• say 'yes' and do something you would not normally do, or
• say 'no' and don't do something that you always do.

These should be small changes, nothing drastic. Every day make a small change and write it down in at the bottom or your diary. I know it seems odd, but believe me, this is a powerful technique. When you make small changes to your everyday routine you will feel uncomfortable at first, but this feeling soon passes. Every time you make a change you build resilience to feeling slightly uncomfortable and it soon stops being a problem. It also puts things into perspective when you realise that many of the rules that you have been following slavishly don't really matter and most of the time nobody even notices the changes you make.

You might:

• leave your phone at home
• wear odd socks
• let somebody else chair the meeting
• wear your watch on the other arm

Get yourself out of your comfort zone and you will have much more insight into all those petty little rules that you inflict on your life and the stress it causes when you violate these insignificant rules.

'I know that it seems really small, but I have driven the kids to school using a different route every day this week. I didn't realise how important it was to me to drive the one way to school every day, until I tried to go a different way. It was really hard at first, but nothing happened and each day it got easier!' -Janet

The important thing it to make it fun. You'll love finding freedom from all those petty rules.

BITESIZE

You have all the food knowledge that you need to recover from food chaos, and you have a tool, the Food and Mood Diary, to help you find out what works for your body and what works against your body.

You know the following:

- How to use your Food and Mood Diary to identify patterns which stabilise the food chaos and patterns which lead to bingeing and purging.

- How to break down the power of rules and building flexibility into your life using the yes/no technique and writing it in your Food and Mood Diary.

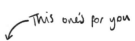
This one's for you

WHAT I LEARNED... WHAT I WILL DO...

CHAPTER SEVEN

SETTING YOURSELF UP FOR SUCCESS

Before you plunge into the programme, it is always best to put in place some relapse recovery techniques. It's important to recognise that up-front recovery is seldom a straight line. There are bumps and setbacks along the way. Keep in mind that lapses are to be expected and therefore, you should have a plan for how to get back on track quickly when you have a lapse. The key to this is eliminating the 'I've blown it' feeling which turns a simple lapse into a collapse and a full-blown binge. During recovery, the mantra you keep saying to yourself is:

IMPROVEMENT NOT PERFECTION

If you keep improving no matter how many setbacks you have, you will recover.

MOTIVATION

SETTING YOURSELF UP FOR SUCCESS

The key to relapse mastery is having the motivation to carry on in the face of adversity, learning from your mistakes and keeping on until new, positive habits are firmly in place. Most people mistake motivation for willpower, but there are many sources of motivation. Some set you up for success, while others will end in yet another failure.

As the old saying goes:

'There are two ways to move a donkey. Whack it over the backside with a stick or dangle a bunch of carrots in front of its nose.'

Both are useful in the right place, but it is important you know which approach works in different situations. For example, a whack over the backside will make a donkey move quickly. Unfortunately, it will move in any direction – as long as it is away from the pain. The problem is, the further it gets from the pain, the less motivated it is to move. But, by dangling a carrot in front of its nose, once you get the donkey going in the direction you want, it will follow the carrots until it gets to the destination.

You have probably been motivated to pick up this book by a metaphorical whack up the backside. But, it is the carrot of recovery that will keep you pushing on when times get difficult. As you get nearer and nearer to your goal (using the carrot method), your motivation will grow and grow.

What you chose to motivate you can have a major impact on your recovery. Here are examples of what happens when you choose the stick method and what happens when you choose the carrot method to motivate your recovery.

BACK TO SQUARE ONE

I had a patient called Elaine who was motivated by a 'whack up the backside', a position of self-hate. Elaine hated herself for bingeing and she hated being out of control and the guilt, so she was desperate to stop. It was simply not her; she prided herself on her willpower in every area of her life, except when it came to food.

So, Elaine got motivated and set some rules in place to start to recover. Elaine could have pushed on to her goal, but after 4 days, she got tempted to eat chocolate. Just the thought of it made her anxious. As she became more and more anxious, she was ever more fearful that she would break down, eat some chocolate and she would hate herself and feel a failure. The stress increased until the only way to stop thinking about chocolate was to eat some. 'Just one or two squares,' she told herself, but before she knew it, she had eaten the whole bar. On top of this, the guilt and the feeling of having failed increased and the lapse lead to 'I've blown it – I might as well eat my head off,' and escalated into a full-blown binge.

The next day, full of remorse and good intentions, Elaine vowed to try again – harder. In effect, Elaine was 'back to square one'. Except she was in an even worse place, because now Elaine had another concrete example of what a failure she was.

Does Elaine's experience match your experience about bingeing? Do you recognise yourself in Elaine's story? Do you know how it feels to try, and try really hard, only to finish up back at square one? It doesn't have to be like that. Maybe the problem is not your willpower, but the place from where you have drawn your motivation. You could learn a different strategy, one that does not end up in yet another binge.

LEARNING EXPERIENCE

Paul, another of my patients, showed a different approach which was much more effective than Elaine's. It is a stark example of how where you draw motivation from can have a major effect on your success.

Paul was motivated to stop bingeing, but he chose to be motivated by the carrot method. He was doing it to improve his life from a position of self-love. Paul wanted to stop bingeing so he could buy something he really wanted – A blue Toyota GT 86.

I asked Paul how stopping bingeing could buy him a sports car and he said, I spend around £100 ($130) a week on binge food. That's £400 ($520) per month. If I trade in my car, I can easily afford an MR2 and probably put money in the bank.

Have you ever estimated how much you spend on binges and thought of what you could spend that money on instead?

Paul got motivated, set some rules in place and started the recovery programme. Paul, like Elaine could have pushed on to his goal, but he also got tempted. The difference is that when Paul got tempted there was not much emotion involved because, unlike Elaine, there was not much at stake. If Elaine ate chocolate, she put her whole identity at risk. Bingeing for her would be, in her words, 'disgusting', she would have her whole moral self on the line. You can imagine how frightening it was for Elaine to be tempted by chocolate.

For Paul, on the other hand, a lapse meant that he was the price of one chocolate bar further away from buying that GT86. There simply was not enough at stake to get worked up about. Instead of getting all emotional and turning the lapse into a collapse, Paul identified what was tempting him to eat chocolate. He said that his girlfriend worked odd hours and when he was in the flat on his own, he had the urge to eat chocolate because he was feeling a little lonely and bored. Paul turned the lapse into a learning opportunity and thought of alternatives to bingeing, like going out with a friend or watching football whenever he was tempted in the future.

The key difference here was that Paul did not feel all the anxiety that Elaine felt. For her, it was another all-enveloping moral failure leading to a binge. For Paul, it was a small, isolated, rather unimportant lapse, which taught him about his triggers.

Who do you think had the best chance of recovering? Who had the best strategy? I helped both of them to recover, but for Elaine it was a long, painful and torturous journey. Whereas Paul just stopped bingeing and hardly ever thought about it again.

SET YOURSELF UP FOR SUCCESS

Before you start your recovery journey, ask yourself this one very important question:

Why do you want to change?

What is the first thing that pops into your mind? Write it down here:

Be honest now, are you motivating yourself with a 'stick'? Do you hate yourself for bingeing, for feeling totally out of control and watching your self-confidence and self-esteem evaporate?

In many ways, this is trying to be motivated by a threat. 'If I don't change, this is what will happen to me.' If you use the stick to motivate yourself, you are almost certainly setting yourself up to fail. Don't do that.

Instead use the carrot method. This will motivate you with a promise. 'If I change, I will get all of this.' In Paul's case, it was a sports car. But what about you? What does the prospect of change promise you?

Think about what you are going to get once you are recovered. What would your life be like? Spend a little time imagining what change promises to you. Go back to your pre-meeting questionnaire and see what you put in question 4:

If you could change one thing what would it be?

Imagine what your life would be without this bingeing. Write it down and use this as the 'carrot' to motivate you.

How would I feel?	
How would other People think about me?	
What would I be able to achieve?	

Now look at what you have written for question 5:

What was the last straw that made you look for help?

Imagine what your life would be like if this last straw moment was only a distant memory:

How would I feel?	
How would other People think about me?	
What would I be able to achieve?	

You know that recovery is seldom straightforward. You will have lapses and the important thing is to firstly, expect them and secondly, recover from them as quickly as possible.

You now know the way you motivate yourself can have a big influence on your chances of lapsing.

- Set yourself up for success by being motivated by the carrot of self-love, motivated by the promise of what you will get once you have recovered.

- This will turn lapses into learning experiences instead of 'I've blown it' experiences that end up back at square one.

All you have to do now is put it all into practice. This is a lot to take in, so stop here and spend some time working on building a sound foundation of your recovery. In the next chapter, we will discuss what experience has taught you, then we will move on to tackle other areas which provide energy to your eating disorder.

This one's for you

WHAT I LEARNED... WHAT I WILL DO...

CHAPTER EIGHT

ENDING FOOD CHAOS

Before you continue to the psychological aspects of your condition, I can't emphasis enough how important it is that you spend time stabilising your body and ending food chaos. This will provide a firm foundation on which to build your recovery. In this chapter I will explain how to use your Food and Mood Diary to interpret what works for your body and what works against your body.

Before we go any further, make a note of your impressions of your progress so far.

How did it go?	
How did you feel?	
Did anything suprise you?	
Have you noticed anything different?	

WHAT DOES YOUR DIARY TELL YOU?

Take a little time and go over your week's diary, highlighting what worked, what didn't work, what was easy, what was hard. This way you can review the week as a whole, enabling you to be more objective about what the diary highlights.

I know that this can seem a little daunting at first. So, here is what I look for, to give you a few pointers of how to interpret your diary.

FOOD AND MOOD DIARY

Date								
Time	Food & Drink	Where	Hunger Level	Mood & State of Mind	B	P	Context	Today's Summary

HOW TO READ YOUR FOOD AND MOOD DIARY.

Here is what I look for when going through my client's diaries with them. Once you have a few days filled in, look back at what you have written each day. This will give you a little distance so that you can be more objective when analysing your diary. Read your diary from right to left in this order.

Today s Summary:

The first thing I look at is what has been written in 'Today's Summary'. It should give you an overall snapshot of the day. Then check back with what actually happened that day, to see if the summary accurately reflects the events. I often find my clients tend to focus on the things that did not go to plan and ignore the things that did. This results in an overly pessimistic summary. If the summary is less than positive, have a look at the annotations. If the day is full of smiley faces, how bad could the day have really been?

Take note of what did not go to plan, but also make a note of the many things that did go to plan.

P:

If my patient is bulimic, the next column I check is the 'P' to see if they have been purging. If they haven't, it is important that they mark the fact. Some use a smiley face in the column, others stick on a star or write 'purge-free day' across the top of the diary. Whatever way you choose to mark the progress is not important, the fact that you mark it is. If you are bulimic and have not marked you purge-free days, do it now. If you have purged, you probably have had a binge, so the next place to look is the 'Binge' column (B).

B:

I look at the 'Binge' column in the same way as with the 'P' column. It is important to mark if you have not binged that day.

It is interesting to examine what you consider a binge. You can tell the difference between overeating and bingeing. This is very important for your recovery, because for many people, overeating is a trigger to bingeing. I'm sure you already know the difference between bingeing and overeating, and we both know it is little to do with the amount of food you eat. The key is to consciously know the difference.

You know how it goes: you overeat something and think to yourself, 'I've blown it, I might as well be hung for a sheep as a lamb,' and turn an overeating event into a binge. Become an expert in identifying the difference between overeating and bingeing. This will enable you to say to yourself 'I've just overeaten, so what? The important thing is I didn't binge, which is great.' Consciously knowing the difference will help you to control what was in the past a triggering event.

Pattern finding:

The next step is to find out which patterns in your diary lead to bingeing and purging and which patterns lead to stability.

- If you have been purging – look for patterns that lead you to purge.
- If you have been bingeing – look with for patterns that lead you to binge.
- If you have been stable, binge- and purge-free – look for patterns that lead you to stability.

As you examine your diary you will see the consequences of different patterns of eating and feel them at a deep level. It is not just somebody giving you good advice. It is you that is feeling, firsthand, just what happens when you follow a certain pattern. The idea is that you feel in your heart exactly what works well for you and your body and do more of that. You will also see what patterns lead to food chaos for you and your body and do less or, better still, stop doing that.

Hunger levels:

This is a very important recovery indicator. Many of you have probably spent years restricting what you eat. In doing so, you may no longer respond to internal cues that you are getting hungry. If this is you, you might find lots of 1s and 5s.

Going through life either not hungry or suddenly ravenous is very disconcerting. Most of the time you are happily getting on with your day when suddenly you are starving. Hunger at this level is associated with low blood sugar levels, anxiety and impulsivity. This is not a good place to make rational choices. You only know you have to eat and eat now. It can feel like you have no control over the situation.

When you see a 5, notice how long it has been since your last meal and make a note of how you were feeling.

As you get more experienced and structured eating becomes a habit, you will see a lot more 2s, 3s and 4s. This puts you in a much better place to make rational choices and gives you a lot more control. For example: 'Hmm, I am at level 2 hungry, I'd better find something to eat in the next hour before I get really hungry.'

It also results in much more positive feelings in the Mood column.

As you work through your diary, you identify exactly what works for you and also what works against you. You begin to feel it in your heart. Once this has happened you will get an instinctive understanding of how to prevent things going so far that they reach hunger level 5. As you become more sensitised to your hunger cues, you will know when you are at level 3 and do something about it.

Where:

Check where the food has been eaten. This gives a little context to identify problem areas and to put in place strategies to overcome them. For example, many of my clients have real problems bingeing in the car. June did a lot of traveling between clients in her car. If she had binge food in the car, she would binge on it and then pull over into a garage and purge. She would then buy more binge food and repeat.I suggested that it might be an idea not to have binge food in the car. June had tried that, but it made her so stressed, knowing she did not have any binge food to hand in case she needed it. She would obsessively think about food until she felt compelled to pull over, buy food, binge and purge.

I suggested to June that she put her binge food in the boot (trunk) of the car and told her, 'Any time you needed to binge, simply stop the car, go to the boot and binge to your heart's content.' 'But I won't do that,' said June. 'Maybe not, but you could,' I replied. That was the last time she binged in the car. The food in the car was too tempting, no food in the car was too stressful. Food in the boot was neither tempting nor stressful. The added advantage that June built up the habit of the car being a 'safe place', a place where she never even thought about food, let alone bingeing.

Food and drink:

At this stage I am not too worried what you've eaten. The first stage is to get a pattern of regular eating so you can feel the benefit of stable blood sugar levels. You can always tweak what you are eating once good, regular eating habits are established.

That said, go through what you have eaten and do a very rough calorie count. Often, although you may feel like you have been eating far too much, you are still eating less than what you had earlier calculated was a healthy amount. Having a rough guess of how many calories you have eaten removes the fear of thinking you have been overeating and, at the same time, lets you to how much you have been undereating in the past.

Time:

Have you eaten breakfast? If so, mark it with a tick or smiley face. If not, look to see the knock-on consequences throughout the day. Have you eaten approximately every three hours? If so, mark it. If not, look to see the knock-on consequences throughout the day.

YES/NO EXERCISE

Have a look at the small changes you made in the past week in the yes/no exercise. Ask yourself:

- Was it harder than you thought it would be?

- What was the most difficult thing you did?

- Did anyone notice that you had made the change?

- Did it make a difference to you?

- What did you find out that most surprised you?

- Did you find that some of the changes worked better?

- Did it get easier and more fun the more you did it?

- Do you think it will now be a fun part of your life?

- Do you now think that Richard Carlson's book, 'Don't Sweat the Small Stuff', has a point?

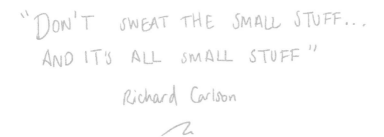

"Don't sweat the small stuff...
and it's all small stuff"
Richard Carlson

PRACTISE ANALYSING FOOD AND MOOD DIARIES

Before trying to analyse your own diary, have a look for patterns in the following two diaries. What do they tell you? Needless to say, these were diaries of clients before they had started Structured Eating.

Sarah, a 30-year-old woman

Time	Food & Drink	Where	Hunger Level	Mood & State of Mind	B	P	Context	Today's Summary
09:00	Overnight Oats	Work	Felt hungry after the gym	Good			Felt full after eating	Felt really rubbish and overfull when I went to bed.
13:00	Naked burrito bowl	Cafe	Hungry	Good			Ate out with colleagues. Felt full after eating.	Tried to vomit
14:00	Donut	Desk	A bit hungry	Good			Wanted something sweet	
19:00	Haloumi wrap and 2 packets of chicken	In front of TV	Hungry	Fed up, been let down	B	P	Ate far too much but couldn't stop and felt awful afterwards.	
	2 slices of toast and Nutella				B	P	Mindless eating in front of the TV.	

You might notice Julie's diary doesn't use numbers for hunger levels. This is OK to get started, but I would recommend she uses numbers in future weeks. Use numbers in your diary, they make it much easier for you to understand what's going on.

From what you have learned so far about the number of calories you need to be healthy and the importance of structured eating, what would you advise Sarah to do?

If I was working through this diary with Sarah, I would ask her to look at what she had written. In her 'Today's summary', she 'felt really rubbish and overfull when I went to bed and tried to vomit.'

Looking objectively at Sarah's diary, do you think that she had had a terrible day being out of control or basically she had had 3 meals and a couple of snacks?

My thoughts:

- Overall, including the binges, Sarah probably hadn't overeaten. Clearly, she thought she had and tried to get rid of the binge using laxatives and attempting to vomit.
- I would explain what is a reasonable amount for a person to eat in order to be healthy.
- Going 5 hours between meals probably wasn't a good idea for her.
- Important for her to stabilise her blood sugar levels using structured eating.
- I would also explain how purging by using vomiting or laxatives does not get rid of the calories from bingeing (see chapter on Bulimia).

Here is a day from Julie's diary. She is 35 years old. What does it tell you?

Time	Food & Drink	Where	Hunger Level	Mood & State of Mind	B	P	Context	Today's Summary
10:00	½ cream eclair	Kitchen		2 days out of date only ate half	B			Been preoccupied with thoughts about food the whole day. Feel completely hopeless and anxious. Feel it's pointless trying to resist the urge to binge.
11:00	Hot lemon water. Bran flakes	Kitchen		Trying to eat normally today. Struggling with thoughts of bad foods	B			
14:00	½ cream eclair	Kitchen		Did well to last this long	B			
15:00	Egg & chips	Kitchen		Don't feel ready to change yet.	B			Plan for Tomorrow
18:00	Went to the shops to buy binge food	In the car		On the way home feeling relief.				
19:45	Packet of crisps	Kitchen		Feelings of relief are turning to feelings of disgust	B	P		
20:30	Goats cheese bread roll	Kitchen			B			
20:40	Pizza and chips More M&M's	Kitchen		Feeling bloated and pains in my stomach. I can't carry on like this	B			
22:00	Full bag of M&Ms, half bag of popcorn, big bar of chocolate	Kitchen			B			

A different problem here, but what areas would you advise Julie to concentrate on the following week?

In her 'Today's summary', she had 'been preoccupied with thoughts about food the whole day. Feel completely hopeless and anxious. Feel it's pointless trying to resist the urge to binge.'

My thoughts:

Knowing what you know now, would you be surprised if Julie had felt any other way? It's totally understandable.

- Julie had eaten nothing but an éclair and some bran flakes (approx. 400 calories) up to 3:00 pm.
- If Julie had eaten at 10:00 pm the previous evening, that would be 17 hours with very little to eat.
- It is no wonder that she was ready to eat egg and chips (fries), and from there it was all downhill.
- Any structure in Julie's eating patterns are likely to cause a dramatic improvement in how she is feeling, both physically and mentally.

ANALYSING YOUR FIRST WEEK FOOD AND MOOD DIARY

It's always easy to solve other people's problems, but it is often more difficult with our own. Bearing in mind your own experience of the past week and the examples of Sarah and Julie, have a look at your diary and see what it tells you.

Did you write 'Food is Medicine' on each page of your diary?
Did you mark things 'well done' with a smiley face etc.?
Did you write what you did in the Yes/No homework in your diary?

Today's Summary:

Does your summary match what is written down in the diary?
What went to plan?

P:

If you are bulimic, did you purge that day?
If not, mark with ;0)

B:

I look at the Binge column in the same way as with the P column. It is important to mark if you have not binged that day.

Pattern finding

The next step is to find the patterns in your diary which lead to bingeing and/or purging and patterns that lead to stability.

• If you have been purging, were there any patterns that led to a purge?
• Were there any patterns that lead you to binge?
• Were there any patterns that lead to binge-free stability?

Structured eating:

Have you been eating 3 meals a day?
Have you been eating 3 snacks per day?
Are you eating breakfast?
Have you stopped using sweeteners?
Are you drinking diet drinks?
Are you eating low fat/diet versions of food?

What do you notice when you eat in this structured manner?
What happens when you do not eat in a structured manner?

Time:

Have you eaten breakfast?
Have you eaten approximately every 3 hours?

Hunger levels:

Are your hunger levels mainly 1s and 5s?
Are your hunger levels of 2s, 3s and 4s appearing more often?

Food and drink:

Not counting any binges, are you eating enough to be healthy?
Are you surprised how much food you need to eat to be nourished?

Where:

Are there any problem areas where you eat?

LESSONS LEARNED

When I go through the diaries with my patients, they are often quite
apprehensive about what I will think. What they don't know is that I realise
that what I have asked them to do is not just make a few adjustments to how
they are eating. I have requested something far more profound. I am asking
them to turn what they have been doing and believing for years – or even
decades – on its head and try something very different. This can be very
scary. The way to stop bingeing is not through discipline and food rules, but
to nourish your body by eating enough. In many cases, this means eating far
more than they have been eating for a long time.

If you have had a few days when you stuck to structured eating and a few
days when you haven't, you may feel that you have somehow failed. This is
far from the truth. You have not failed because both sets of information – the
successful days and the not-so-successful days – in your diary are extremely
useful. The diary is such a powerful tool because it allows you to experience

the effect of structured eating and the effect of restriction in real time. It also gives you the chance to reflect at your leisure on the patterns which lead you to food chaos and which patterns lead to stability. This is not just an academic exercise to convince you that structured eating works. This way you will know in your heart that it works and whatever you do in the future will only emphasise the fact.

As you calmly review your Food and Mood Diary, think about what it tells you. Here are a few suggestions of what you may take from your diaries. Feel free to add anything that you think will help you in the following weeks.

ACTIONS FOR NEXT WEEK	
I have learnt	
What works for me	
What works against me	
What I will do differently next week	

SUMMARY OF YOUR FIRST WEEK

How did the first week go? I suspect that it rather depends on how successfully you applied the Structured Eating. Don't worry if you found structured eating difficult at first. It flies in the face of everything you have been told before. We all approach things differently. When you go to the beach, some people run into the sea and get totally wet, whereas others are a bit more cautious and tiptoe into the sea, bit by bit. Whichever way you go about doing things, once you are in the sea you can start to enjoy the experience. It's the same with structured eating: once you stabilise your blood sugar levels, you will feel the benefit. If you're a tiptoe kind of person, just cut yourself a bit of slack, there's no rush. The main thing is to concentrate on eating every three hours or so and filling in your diary.

Stabilising your blood sugar levels is a key part of the treatment. You will gain great benefits from this one technique and it is well worth spending a little getting it right before moving on to the next stage.

Once eating every three hours is embedded as a habit and you are getting more in tune with your hunger cues, you can always tweak the structured eating as you grow more confident.

If you jumped right into structured eating, I am assuming you are pleasantly pleased by its effects. Many people look back after the first week and realise they have not binged at all or have at least seen a dramatic reduction in bingeing. This often comes as a surprise and may leave you feeling a bit foolish that you haven't done it before. Well, don't feel bad! It is easy to be so immersed in what you are trying so hard to do that it's difficult to see the wood for the trees.

After a week of structured eating, Jean said to me:

'Is that it? Is that all it took for me to stop bingeing? I can't believe that I've been such a fool. All the time & energy I've spent beating myself up trying to stop bingeing and all I had to do was eat enough. I can't believe it, that I've been such a fool.'

There is much more work to do but getting your blood sugar levels stable is the foundation of the rest of your recovery. It is worth spending time getting this right before moving to the next stage.

You are now in a strong position to understand how different patterns of eating affects your body.

- You now know how to analyse your Food and Mood Diary.

- You have practised analysing two sample Food and Mood Diaries.

- You now know how to systematically interpret your Food and Mood Diary to find patterns.

- You will have identified patterns that lead to stability – do more of these.

- Some of you will have identified patterns that lead to food chaos – stop doing these.

This one's for you

WHAT I LEARNED... WHAT I WILL DO...

CHAPTER NINE

THE CRITICAL VOICE

Now that you have stopped the food chaos and stabilised your blood sugar levels, it's time to move on to the psychological factors that maintain your eating disorder. We start with the big one – that critical voice in your head, sometimes known as the poison parrot on your shoulder. We all know what the Critical Voice is. We have all heard it loud and clear. But for the most part, we can say to ourselves, 'Don't be silly!' and shrug it off. But when somebody develops an eating disorder, this critical voice becomes more and more powerful, until it seems to take control over your life.

It can start as a friendly, cajoling voice that whispers in your ear: 'Go on, have another cookie, you deserve it, you've had a tough day.' But after a few cookies, the voice can suddenly turn into a shouting rebuke: 'What's wrong with you? Are you a greedy child or something? Don't you know what's good for you? You should be ashamed eating all those cookies.' As it gets louder and harsher it can have a devastating effect on a person's self-esteem as they feel less and less in control and more and more at its mercy. I'm sure you recognise this voice and realise that it is one of the factors that is keeping you stuck in your eating disorder. You may feel powerless to do anything about it. You probably didn't realise that with a little help you can shut that voice up. But you can.

I know this seems a dream at the moment, but just think about how life would be in the future when the voice talks to you and you can say to yourself, 'That's interesting, but don't worry, it'll be fine,' and the voice calms down and you can move on. In order to control the voice, you need to know a little about what it is trying to do and turn it from your enemy to your friend.

THE 'THINKING BRAIN' AND THE 'EMOTIONAL BRAIN'.

The brain is a complex organ that has many parts, most of which operate effectively below our level of consciousness. They simply happen: our hair grows, our nails grow, our heart beats at the right rhythm etc. Where the critical voice is concerned, it is useful to think of the brain having two parts: the **Thinking Brain** and the **Emotional Brain.**

The thinking brain is what makes us different from other mammals. It is here that your personality, values, hopes and dreams are kept. It is here that we consciously use the power of rational thought and can plan for the future. It is also the part of the brain responsible for language.

The emotional brain is responsible for keeping us alive and mostly works at a subconscious level. This part of the brain relies on feelings and intuition to keep us safe. It works very quickly (much faster than the thinking brain) and can warn us of dangerous situations. When the emotional brain is feeling under threat it can use a variety of methods to change our behaviour and keep us safe.

The two parts of the brain are joined with a bridge, so when the emotional brain becomes frightened it can alert the thinking brain to act as a mediator to assess the situation.

Although both the thinking brain and the emotional brain are part of us, the two have very different agendas and sometimes can clash. The thinking brain has rational thoughts and can make decisions based in reality, whereas the emotional brain makes decisions based on feelings, hunches and gut instinct. This can sometimes cause confusion, because the emotional brain does not have access to language. So, it uses your voice, the voice you use when you are mulling things over in your thinking brain. Understandably, this can seem like the same voice, but it's not. It is working on guesses and hunches rather than considering the situation. Unless you can separate the 'thinking brain voice' from the 'emotional brain voice' it can seem like you are constantly contradicting yourself. One of my clients recently described this as:

'It's like I have two people sitting on my shoulders having an argument all the time. One says one thing and the other says another and I'm just stuck between them. It's awful, I just can't think straight.'

Jean

TECHNIQUES TO SOOTHE THE CRITICAL VOICE

There are many ways of shutting down that critical voice. Here are two which my clients find very useful in their recovery. Simply having the skill to switch off the voice will allow you to stop feeling like a victim and you will be able to take control of the situation, dramatically reducing the anxiety caused by the voice.

Technique One: The voice is not you.

'The voice is not you' is based on putting a little space between you and your emotions. This space, or distancing, has the effect of tuning down the emotions (so you feel calmer) and it will give you more time to think rationally and to assess the situation objectively.

Step 1: Be alert for the voice

The first step in this technique is to recognise that the voice is NOT you. Knowing this, you must be alert for the voice and spot it as quickly as you can.

If you find your thoughts urging you to do something that you don't want to do, it's probably the voice. You can check by resisting. If the voice doesn't get its own way it escalates the pressure and soon gets aggressive, louder and harsher in its judgements. Basically, if you are feeling horrible – it's probably the voice.

Top Tip

When you start to be critical of yourself, ask yourself this question – 'Would I talk to anyone else like that?' If you wouldn't, it's probably the voice.

Step 2: Separate the voice

This step is to separate the voice from yourself. Make the voice talk to you in the second person. So, if the voice says, 'What's the use? I always mess everything up.' Change it to say, 'What's the use? You always mess everything up.' This changes the dynamic from you talking to yourself to the voice talking to you. This makes the voice seem almost as if a separate entity is talking to you. It is not your thoughts but simply your emotional response, which is based on feelings and hunches rather than reality.

When you make this step, the power of the voice will dramatically reduce, your emotions will drop, and you feel calmer.

This is the very powerful first step to separate the voice from you. It has the effect of making the voice seem like someone is attacking you, and in most cases when we are attacked, we fight back. Or at least we assess whether what has been said has any basis in reality. Having the ability to make this assessment reinforces that fact that although it doesn't feel like it at times, the thinking brain has the power to make decisions.

The emotional part can be a great asset to our lives, but its decisions are based on feelings and they are often wrong. It must always be kept in its place by the rational part.

I am always reminded of the old saying: 'Fire is a good servant but a bad master.' In other words, when we are in charge of fire and use it to heat our homes, fire is a good servant. But if fire gets out of hand and takes charge, it can burn our homes down. Don't let the emotional brain voice get out of control.

Separating the voice gives you the chance to realise that it's the voice talking, NOT what you are thinking. Realising 'the voice is NOT you' provides a little distance from the emotion and has the effect of reducing anxiety, so you feel calmer. You are in charge and you can hear what the voice is actually saying and assess whether it's worth listening to or not without the confusion of emotion.

Step 3 : Give the voice a name

The next step is to increase the separation by giving the voice a name. Once it has a name it becomes further separated from you, with a personality of its own. Just let a name bubble up from your subconscious. Some people think of a person's name, such as Eric; others chose a descriptive name, such as Piggy or Scramble. It doesn't matter what you call it as long as it's relevant to you. Giving the voice a name further distances it from you, making it feel like a separate entity in your mind. It's not you that's thinking these horrible thoughts about yourself, but it's 'Piggy' saying them. This further distancing makes Piggy's irrational ranting much easier to identify and dismiss.

Step 4: Throw your voice out

Once you can separate the voice and give it a name, you can metaphorically throw it out of your body. Instead of listening to the voice in your head, imagine the voice is talking to you from about four feet in front of you. This further enhances the distancing, by giving the impression you are talking to another person. If you can, imagine what the voice looks like as a person or a thing. If you can imagine Piggy standing in front of you saying those awful words, it increases the distancing effect.

Step 5 : Speak the words out loud

Speak **out loud** exactly the words that the voice is saying. By speaking the words out loud you are forced into using the rational part of your brain (language is only contained in the rational part of the brain). When your rational brain is engaged, you are in a better place to decide whether what the voice is telling you has any basis in reality or is an overreaction to a perceived threat. Sometimes you will be surprised when you speak the words out loud, hearing how some of the things the voice says are so ridiculous. The voice is simply reacting to fear (real or imagined) and you can decide whether there is an actual threat or not. Then ask yourself this -"Is there any basis in reality for what the voice is saying?"For the vast majority of the time it will be obvious that what the voice is saying is rediculous and has no basis in reality. Once you realise this, the power of what it is saying will fade and the voice will fade with it.' Just let it fade away and move on.

Step 6: Soothe the voice - let it work with you

It's like when you were a child in bed and you felt safe, knowing your parents were downstairs. In some ways, the thinking part of the brain has almost a parental responsibility to calm the situation and the voice. You can soothe the voice by reassuring it that you have listened to what it has to say, assessed the situation and everything is under control.

After a few seconds, ask yourself, 'What is the [the name you have given the voice] saying now?' You can do this internally.

Oh, she's back in her box now! Tracey

Basically, all you are doing is saying 'I've got this' and checking in to see that all is OK and to reassure your emotions that you have everything under control.

I know that this seems a bit woo-woo, but I don't care. All I know is that it works. The good thing is that you can use this technique in other parts of your life where you are plagued by an internal critical voice that makes you hesitant to change.

Summary of 'the voice is not you' technique

- Be alert for the voice.
- Separate the voice.
- Give the voice a name.
- Throw the voice out in front of you.
- Speak the words the voice says out loud.
- Ask yourself whether what it says has any basis in reality.
- Let the voice fade.

Technique Two the Joystick
This can be fun

Step 1: Be alert for the voice

The first step in the technique is to recognise the voice in the same way as in 'The voice is NOT you' technique and give the voice a name.

Step 2: Pick up a pen

When you notice the voice, pick up a pen or pencil (or anything that fits in your hand) and pretend that it is a computer joystick.

Step 3: Move the voice with the joystick

Just like when you play a video game, you move the character with the joystick. Point the joystick to the left, watch the voice go to where you point and listen to how it changes.

Now just have fun moving the voice around and noticing how it changes. Move it to the right and make it change colour. Does the voice change? Make it spin. What happens? Move it to the left. What happens? Where do you move it so that it goes quieter? Where does it stop shouting? Where does it become reasonable? Where does it just disappear?

Once I had explained the technique, I tried this with Jean, who called the voice Erica. Once Jean became aware of Erica, she picked up a pen.

Me: Where do you hear Erica?
Jean: Just behind my right ear and she is shouting into it.
Me: Take your joystick and move Erica in front of you and what do you notice?
Jean: She doesn't like it, she is very angry, but it doesn't feel the same.
Me: Now take the joystick and move her further away, to the other side of the room. Now what do you notice?
Jean: She is getting madder, but although she is shouting, I can hardly hear her.
Me: Try moving her to the left. What do you notice?
Jean: Just the same.
Me: Try moving her to the right. What do you notice?
Jean: Getting really quiet now.
Me: Let Erica move to the right and far away. When you can't hear her, let me know.
Jean: That's amazing ... I can't hear her at all.

Step 4: Imaginary joystick

After a few trials you will find that you don't need to pick up a pen, all you have to do is imagine you have a joystick in your hand and move the voice to where you are most comfortable listening to it. Or simply make it go away.

Summary of the 'Joystick' technique

- Be alert for the voice.
- Separate the voice.
- Give the voice a name.
- Use the joystick to move the voice around.
- Notice how the voice changes when you move it to different positions.
- Find out where you can put the voice, so that it gets quieter and quieter and finally fades away.
- Let the voice fade and move on with your life.

BITESIZE

- You now have an understanding that the different parts of your brain have different agendas. You might have a long-term goal of losing weight. Another part of your brain wants you to stay alive and might interpret the lack of calories as a famine. You know how to recognise the difference between your thinking brain and your emotional brain.

- You also have two very powerful techniques to quieten the emotional brain and give your thinking brain space to think, space to acknowledge the threat that is perceived by the emotional brain, space to assess whether it is valid or not and then space to decide the best course of action to pursue your thinking brain goals.

- Knowing you have control means you have the choice as to whether to listen to the voice or not. Feeling stuck is very stressful. Choice is a very liberating thing – grasp it in every area of your life.

This one's for you

WHAT I LEARNED... WHAT I WILL DO...

CHAPTER TEN

HANDLING YOUR EMOTIONS WITHOUT USING FOOD

Negative emotions produce a lot of stress and anxiety, which provides the energy that feeds your eating disorder. This stress can come from two distinct sources: physical and psychological. When we don't eat enough, we put the body under unmanageable physical stress and it responds automatically with the stress response. Psychologically, you put your body under stress when you impose unreasonable rules on yourself. Just thinking about the rules, being tempted, being anxious in case you break the rules, feeling guilty when you break the rules and then beating yourself up for being so weak, causes stress and anxiety.

The good news is the techniques you have learned so far will have already reduced this stress considerably. If you have successfully stabilised your blood sugar levels with structured eating, a great deal of the stress felt by the body physically is starting to subside. By taking control over the voice you will also have significantly reduced your psychological stress levels. If you have been using food as a way of managing the emotions that cause you stress (and everyone does to some extent), then it is essential to learn other more positive skills and techniques that will both reduce the stress you feel and starve your eating disorder (pun intended) of the energy that maintains it.

TECHNIQUES TO COPE WITH STRESS

To allay your fears about how you will cope with life's challenges without bingeing, it would be useful for you to learn a few positive techniques to: reduce stress by being able to choose what to worry about and forget the rest; become less sensitive to what people say or what life throws up at you; and having the tools to switch off the triggers that usually lead to bingeing.

Once you have learned these techniques you will no longer have the need to self-medicate by bingeing.

In this section, you will learn how to:

- Choose what to get worried about and what to just let go.
- How to be less sensitive to what life throws at you.
- How to deal with triggers.

Before jumping into the techniques, I want to discuss how some people are just good with stress. We all know people who can handle stress. Do you ever wonder how they do it? Do they seem strong and disciplined with an inner calm during difficult times? In contrast, how does that make you feel? If you ask them for advice about how you should cope with a difficult situation, they might tell you to 'forget about it', 'just let it go over your head', or to 'put it behind you'. But how? You don't have the iron willpower that these people seem to have. I'll let you into a secret: the last thing these people are doing is using willpower. When they say 'forget about it' they mean it, they just forget about something and, hey presto, it's gone. If you forget about something it is no longer stressful. If they 'let it go over their heads', they have done just that; they have let the problem fly over their heads without it sticking to them. By putting it behind them, they have left the matter in the past, where it belongs.

Throughout my career I learned a lot about the difference in the way that people handle stress and anxiety. Much to my surprise, it was nothing to do with personality or strength of character, but rather a set of easily learned techniques. Learn them and they will dramatically reduce your stress and anxiety – today.

What has constantly struck me in my work is that, as a group, people with eating disorders are all nice, caring people, and I suppose this is their downfall. Let me explain. They often feel inadequate because they cannot handle the stresses that life throws at them without having to resort to bingeing, a thing they hate that undermines their self-esteem. They look around and see others with similar problems, who are simply taking them in their stride. They often feel that in comparison they were weak-willed or have a character flaw that makes them unable to cope with life without using bingeing as a crutch.

I know that there was nothing wrong with their character, they just need a little knowledge and to learn a few positive skills to help them get through life with less stress and anxiety.

The first bit of knowledge you need to know is that you are only stressed and anxious because you care. Take a moment again to let that sink in.

You only get stressed IF YOU CARE. I'll bet if you went to any town in the country this afternoon, you could find people who can't pay their bills and yet they are having a social drink with friends. They are not stressed because they don't care. They don't care if they can pay their bills or not, they only care that they are enjoying themselves at the time. If you couldn't pay your bills you would care and be stressed out. The last thing you would be spending your time and money on is having a social drink. You would both have the same problem — 'Can't pay my bills' — but have very different reactions. They are having a nice, friendly drink and you are stressed. The difference is that you care about paying your bills and they don't.

Once you realise this it will turn your misconceptions on their head. You will realise that you are not a weak person who can't handle stress. You are feeling stressed because you are a caring, responsible person. I'm not saying you shouldn't care about anything and change your entire personality, I am just letting you know that you are worrying about a problem, not because you are weak, but because you care.

That said, what do you do about it? Well, here is a great technique that will help you to choose what to care and worry about and what to just let go.

Technique One : Choose what you worry about

Choose carefully what you care about. I know this might seem a strange statement, but we can only handle so much stress at any one time, so it's best to pick the most important things, the things you care about, and put your energy into them.

Your 'WORRY GLASS'

We can all handle a certain amount of stress before it becomes unmanageable. A good way to think of this is to imagine that each of us can handle a glassful of stress. This is your 'worry glass'. When the glass is empty, it can take a drip of water and even a splash of water with no problem. It's the same with our stress levels; when we have little or no stress, we can handle a difficult situation easily. However, if the worry glass is full to the brim, the tiniest drop will cause the glass to overflow. If you are feeling a lot of stress, the smallest thing can tip you over the edge, resulting in chronic anxiety or worse. If you can keep your worry glass as empty as possible, you will be able to handle even difficult situations. 'Yep,' you might think, 'but how do you do that?'

You need a strategy to decide how to choose what to put into the worry glass and what to leave out. So, given we can only handle so much stress, I ask you:

What is your strategy to decide what to worry about and what to forget?

This is always fun to ask, because I'll bet most of you have no way of deciding and you didn't know that you could choose. Often it feels like you don't have a choice, stuff happens, and you get stressed: 'It just sort of happens.'

The problem is, unless you have a way to choose what to worry about and what not to worry about, you tend to worry about everything – and I mean everything. Your worry glass simply fills up on its own. If this is you, no wonder it always seems full to the brim and you are in a constant state of stress, which can easily slip into overwhelm. You might not believe you can choose what to put in your worry glass, but you can. It's a skill you can learn with this technique.

Three Question Technique: To Reduce Stress

When something unpleasant happens, simply ask yourself these three questions and they will give you the power to choose whether to worry or, more importantly, whether to just let it go.

QUESTION 1: WHAT'S THE WORST THING THAT CAN HAPPEN?

It helps you to prioritise situations which are both important and urgent. Just ask the question 'What's the worst that can happen?' It is often tempting to catastrophise and jump to the worst conclusion, but take your time. It usually takes a few rounds of questioning in order to dig down to the real consequences.

I once worked with a binge eater called Jean. Every morning, Jean would wake up at 7:00 am and shout up the stairs to her son every 10 minutes, telling him to get up for work. She would get more anxious each time she called him, and he didn't get up. She would do this until 8:00, at which time he jumped out of bed and went to work. By this time, she was beside herself with anxiety and had to sit down for a while. To pull herself together she would have a cup of tea and 'just the one biscuit' and, you've guessed it, once she started, one biscuit lead to another and before she knew it, she was in the throws of a binge.

Me: Why do you call him at 7:00?
Jean: I have to, or he wouldn't get up.
Me: What will happen if he doesn't get up?
Jean: He'll be late for work.
Me: What will happen then?
Jean: If he keeps being late for work, he might lose his job.
Me: What will happen then?
Jean: He won't have any money.
Me: What will happen then?
Jean: Well, he won't be able to go out.
Me: What will happen then?
Jean: I suppose he will have to get another job.

Once Jean realised the worst thing that could happen was that her son might lose his job and have to get another one, she realised that getting him up in the morning wasn't worth getting in a state which led to a binge. In general, applying this rule helps you to understand that most things in life are not worth getting anxious about.

Not everything is a life or death issue. The second question will help you decide how to react to less important situations in life.

QUESTION 2: WILL WE STILL BE TALKING ABOUT IT THIS TIME NEXT WEEK?

During our daily lives, many small things can cause stress, and these can soon add up to a brimming or overflowing glass. For example:

- You accidentally break your mother's ornament.
- You are late for a meal with a friend.

- You give a bad interview.
- You give a presentation that bombs.

Ask yourself 'Will we still be talking about it this time next week?' If you project your mind forward and the answer is 'no', you will achieve some perspective on the matter and realise that the situation is not really important. Therefore, though annoying, not really worth worrying about. One less drop in your worry glass.

The final question is very useful in dealing with people, especially family and those close to us.

QUESTION 3: DO I HAVE ANY POWER IN THIS SITUATION?

The final question is simply to ask yourself, 'Do I have any power in the situation?' If the answer is 'no', remind yourself that:

If you have no power in the situation, you have no responsibility – Calm

You can only worry about things that are your responsibility.

The problem is that often we do not recognise this and feel responsible for things which we have no power to affect.

Where you have responsibility without power – Stress

You simply cannot afford to worry about areas where you have no power. The problem is that we often think we have power in situations where, in fact, we do not. Take the previous example of Jean. She naturally felt that she had, as a mother, some power to influence her son. After all, a son 'should' do what his mother tells him – right. Because she felt she had power in the situation, she felt responsible for her son getting up on time. Jean, at a deep level, thought if she didn't get him up on time, it would be her fault if he lost his job. Jean felt responsibility in a situation where she had no power.

In most cases, we have little power over other people's behaviour. You can ask a person to change (as Jean asked her son to get up), but only they have the power to decide whether to change or not. If they choose not to change, it is proof that you have no power in the situation and you are not responsible for the consequences. THEY are responsible for their actions and they are also responsible for the consequences of their actions. Once Jean realised this, she would give her son a shout at 7:50 and have a cup of tea while he got up (or not).

Life will be much easier if you simply ask yourself the three questions. But much more importantly, an empty glass gives you more room to think about what is really important to you so that you can use your energy in a positive way to improve your life as well as the lives of those around you.

This one's for you

Exercise
Think about something which is causing you a lot of stress/anxiety this week. Write it here:

QUESTION 1: WHAT'S THE WORST THING THAT CAN HAPPEN?

Ask yourself 'is it really that bad?
• Yes, terrible – Prioritise it and put all your efforts into solving or reducing the problem.
• No – Forget about it or put it on low priority.

QUESTION 2: WILL WE STILL BE TALKING ABOUT THIS, THIS TIME NEXT WEEK?

- Yes, we will – Prioritise it and put all your efforts into solving or reducing the problem.
- No, we won't – Forget about it or put it on low priority.

QUESTION 3: DO I HAVE ANY POWER IN THIS SITUATION?

- Yes, I have power – Prioritise it and put all your efforts into solving or reducing the problem.
- No, I do not have any power here – Give the responsibility to those with the power and forget about it or put it on low priority.

Techniques to feel less SENSITIVE

Worrying can be very waring on you and has the potential to cause a lot of unnecessary stress and anxiety. Put simply, sensitive people are easily hurt and feel hurt longer than is necessary, which causes a lot of stress. As you have seen in the previous section it is useful to be able to choose what to get stressed about and what to not get stressed about. If you are sensitive, it also helps to be able to choose when to be sensitive and when to put on an invisible forcefield so that you can understand what is going on without feeling hurt. My clients always love the following technique and they tell me it's not a stress reducing technique but rather, when they use it, stress doesn't happen in the first place.

'SEE YOURSELF IN THE PICTURE' TECHNIQUE

I will explain this technique by using Gemma as an example.

Me: Now Gemma, I would like you to think about something that happened this week that made you smile. Something small, not a big deal, something that you can tell me about.
Gemma: Hmm… OK, yes, I've got something.
Me: What was it?
Gemma: Well, it was just my little girl, she was trying to eat with a knife and fork and it was so cute. It really made me smile.
Me: And when you are thinking about it you can get an image in your mind's eye and you feel happy. Is it like you are looking through your own eyes at her?
Gemma: Yes, it's just like she's in front of me, and she looks so sweet.
Me: And that makes you feel good. Now I want you to do a different thing. I would like you to think of something that made you a bit mad, not a big deal, something or nothing that just made you feel miffed, something that you can tell me about.
Gemma: I was at a meeting and made a suggestion, then someone else said the same thing and got all the credit.
Me: Can you see that now in your mind's eye? Is it like you are at the meeting, looking through your own eyes and seeing everything again?
Gemma: Oh yes.
Me: How does that make you feel?
Gemma: Not good, not good at all.
Me: Well, Gemma, just think about what has just happened. In the space of one minute I've been able to make you feel both happy and angry. Who's got the power in this room over how you feel?
Gemma: Well it should be me.
Me: But who has the power in this room, now, to make you feel happy or sad?

Gemma: Well, I suppose you have.

If you think about what Gemma is telling us. She is going through life, something happens, she feels happy, something else happens, and she feels angry. She is totally at the mercy of events. Things happen, and she reacts, like a cork on a choppy sea.

Me: Who should have the power?
Gemma: Me.
Me: Would you like to learn how to take back the power?
Gemma: Yes.
Me: OK, I would like you to think about that meeting again in your mind's eye. But this time, see yourself in the image.
Gemma: OK.
Me: How does it feel now?
Gemma: That's really strange, everything is the same, but it doesn't feel the same at all. I can see me getting angry (in the image), and I can understand why, but somehow, I just don't feel the anger.
Me: Now see your daughter eating, but see her through your own eyes, like you did when you first saw her being cute. How do you feel?
Gemma: Happy.
Me: That's it. You have a habit of remembering things as though you are seeing them through your own eyes. This is great for happy events because they make you happy. Now all you have to do when things are difficult is to see yourself in the picture.

It's a bit like seeing a fight scene on TV. Someone gets punched and you can imagine what it feels like, but you can't really feel it. We tried several scenarios on Gemma and she soon got into the swing of it.

It is a habitual way of thinking and will take a little time to get used to seeing yourself in the picture. When you remember something and it is unpleasant, just see yourself in the image. Keep practising seeing yourself in the picture when remembering unpleasant situations and it will soon become a habit.

This is how surgeons can cut open your belly, fiddle around with your insides, stitch you up, then go for breakfast. They can distance themselves by using techniques like this. If you think about it, you don't want a surgeon who is hesitant with the scalpel because they are worried they might hurt you. You want them to be able to put their feelings to one side and be decisive.

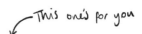
This one's for you

Exercise
Think about something that upsets you when you think about it.
Write it here:

Imagine it.
When you imagine it in your mind's eye, look at what is going on through your own eyes and notice how you feel.

Now imagine the same event, but this time imagine you can see yourself in the picture. It is exactly the same event, but you can see yourself in the image. You can be curious about what is happening as you remember it.

Notice how you feel.

Do you feel like there is a sheet of glass between you and the action? Although you understand how you are feeling in the image, YOU CAN'T ACTUALLY FEEL IT.

How does it feel to have the power to stop your memories making you feel bad, over and over again?

Switching off Triggers technique

Finally, if you use the 3 questions to keep your worry glass empty, and the 'in and out of the picture' technique to become less sensitive to whatever life throws at you, you will be well on the way to starving (pun intended) your eating disorder of the energy that it needs to make your life miserable. But, it still has one powerful weapon in its arsenal – its power to trigger cravings for binge food.

Reframe Technique

To explain how to switch off triggers, I will demonstrate the technique on Lisa.

Me: Lisa, do you have any food that you really can't resist?
Lisa: Well, chocolate I suppose.
Me: And when you think about chocolate, what pops into your mind?
Lisa: A lovely bar of chocolate. (she is pointing about a foot in front of her face, slightly above eye level)
Me: And is it bright?
Lisa: Yes, very bright and colourful.
Me: How big is it?
Lisa: It's big.
Me: Bigger than it is in real life?
Lisa: Yes, much bigger. (looking at the imaginary chocolate and getting quite excited)
Me: And you really like it, don't you? I can see your mouth watering.
Lisa: Yes.
Me: I'll bet you could just eat that now?
Lisa: Oh, yes, I would love some.
Me: Now Lisa, I would like you to push the image away, across the room to that wall over there (about 10 feet). Can you do that?
Lisa: Yes.
Me: What do you notice? Because it is further away, has it got smaller?
Lisa: Yes.
Me: And has the colour gone down. Not as bright as it was?
Lisa: Yes. (not exited now and Lisa's voice is becoming quieter)

Me: I would like you to put a frame around it, like a picture frame. What colour is it?

Lisa: Bright gold.

Me: Bright gold. We keep valuable things in bright gold frames. Can you think of a colour that is more appropriate to something that's not that valuable?

Lisa: It's turned a dull black colour.

Me: A dull black colour. And when we put a frame around something it goes flat. Flat like a photograph. Now it's like a photo, you can make it get smaller, and as it gets smaller you can let the colour drain from the picture. What does it look like now?

Lisa: It's small and not very interesting.

Me: And as you look at the small image that is not very interesting, look at it and watch where it goes when it goes to where we keep things that are not very interesting.

Lisa: It's gone to the left and I can't see it now, it's behind me.

Me: What happened to the craving?

Lisa: I don't know, it's just gone.

Me: Do you care it's gone.

Lisa: No, not really.

That was really remarkable, wasn't it? Within one minute Lisa could trigger a craving and then switch it off, just like that. Now you know whenever you get a craving you can switch it off if you want to.

Let's go over what happened. When you think about something that causes cravings, you see an image of it. If this image is powerful, you see it in front of your face, a little above your eye line, close to your face, larger than life, bright and colourful. Just think about that. Anything that is directly in front of your face, just a foot or so away, takes up all of your vision and attention. It is difficult to think of anything except the image right in front of your face. It takes all your attention, and where we focus gets larger. It is very difficult to think of anything else. While it is there you want it, you really want it. Your eyes are probably bright, you look excited and maybe you are salivating.

The way you think about things can make them irresistible to you and can trigger an out-of-control binge. In Lisa's case, when she thought of chocolate, she imagined it having the following characteristics: it was directly in front of her eyes, larger than life, brightly coloured and in three dimensions.

You can reduce the power these images have over you by changing each of the characteristics, one by one. As you change each characteristic, feel how the impact of the image changes. Make it fun and be curious about how subtle changes in the characteristics can make dramatic changes in how you feel.

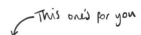

This one's for you

Exercise
Let's practise the 'reframe technique'. You know how to use the technique on trigger foods, but it is not always food that triggers a binge, it could be anything: a type of food, a feeling or the thought of a particular person. It really doesn't matter, the reframe works for anything we find triggering. Let's try it now.

It might be useful to get a friend to help you with this.

Take a little time and let whatever or whoever usually triggers your binge to pop into your mind.

Don't try too hard, just let it pop into your mind.

When you get an image, signal to your friend and get him/her to read these questions. The key is for your friend to take as much time as you need and to repeat exactly what you say back to you.

Friend says:

What do you see?

Where is the image?

I would like you to move the image away to that wall.

Have you noticed as you move it away, it gets smaller?

Do you notice any changes in how that makes you feel?

Now put a frame around the image.

What sort of frame?

Is that appropriate? For example, if it's shiny, gold, sparkly. We usually keep valuable things in shiny, gold, sparkly frames, is it appropriate for this?

What would be more appropriate?

When you put a frame around it, do you notice it goes flat, like a picture.

You can let it get even smaller.

Let the colour drain away

If it's not very interesting, why not let it go to where you keep not very interesting things.

Where did it go?

How do you feel now?

Take a little time and let that feeling grow.

So now you know how to get rid of triggers at will, they have lost their power.

Many people are in two minds when it comes to recovering from their eating disorder. They often wonder 'How will I cope with life if I can't binge?' To tackle this head on and at the same time reduce the energy sources that feed your eating disorder, we have gone through a series of techniques and exercises which will give you positive and powerful ways of coping with stress and emotions. These are life skills and can be applied to any area of your life. Learn them well, and you will have fun and at the same time build up your resilience to meet life head on.

- We discussed the idea of a worry glass and importance of keeping it relatively empty.

- We used the 'Three questions technique' to give you a strategy to decide what to put in the worry glass and what to leave out. This way you can concentrate on the important things and let go of the rest.

- The 'in and out of the picture' technique shows you how to choose when to be sensitive and when not to be so sensitive. The choice NOT to be hurt by life's challenges is very powerful and removes a great deal of anxiety.

- Finally, many people feel at the mercy of triggers. They seem to happen out of the blue and they think they have no choice but to respond. This feeling is a great energy source to your eating disorder. Having the choice to switch off the trigger removes the energy.

Practising these techniques will make you calmer, more confident and more resilient in life in general and will choke off several energy sources of your eating disorder, helping it fade into your past.

MY NOTES

This one's for you

WHAT I LEARNED... WHAT I WILL DO...

CHAPTER ELEVEN

POOR BODY IMAGE

Having a poor body image is one of the key sources of energy for your eating disorder. Feeling bad about how you think you look causes a great deal of negative emotions, provoking anxiety and undermining your self-esteem. A poor body image has the effect of making how you think you look seem much more important than it is, and at the same time reduces the importance of other parts of your life.

Not everyone has issues with body image. In fact, some people have a very positive body image. If you have a good body image, great, you can skip this chapter. But if you are like the vast majority of my clients and have a poor body image, read on.

The aim of this chapter is to put how you 'think' you look into a more realistic perspective, so you see how you look as just one part of who you are (which it is). As you start to value other parts of yourself in a more realistic way, your body image will dramatically improve, ironically because it will matter less. As your life gets bigger and better, it will be just one aspect of who you are.

Indications of poor body image:

- Over checking in mirrors.
- Avoiding mirrors.
- Hundreds of selfies.
- Avoiding being photographed.
- Multiple weighing.
- Pinching parts of the body.
- Constantly seeking reassurance – does my bum look big in this?
- Beauty and the beast thinking – she looks beautiful, so I must look ugly.
- Panicking when you feel fat.
- Mind reading – everyone on the beach will think I look fat.

It's strange that many of these checking behaviours seem contradictory, especially around mirrors and photographs. I have clients who hate having their picture taken but have thousands of selfies on their phones.

These behaviours are very destructive. Both checking and avoidance behaviours cause anxiety (which feeds your eating disorder). Worse still, by constantly repeating the behaviours you are telling the brain that these are very important behaviours. Therefore, they can become entrenched habits that maintain your poor body image.

EFFECTS OF POOR BODY IMAGE

Poor body image has two main effects on your life:

- It makes your life smaller – you avoid more and more things that should be fun.
- How you think you look becomes more and more important – you judge your successes and failures more and more by how you think you look.

HOW MY POOR BODY IMAGE MAKES MY LIFE SMALLER

Poor body image takes the fun out of life.

Have a think and make a list of the things you do not do because you are conscious of how you look or concerned about what other people will think of you.

Things I don't do because of how I look

How does it make you feel looking at this list of things you want to do, but somehow you just can't? Imagine if you had a better body image and you could do all of these things without a second thought – how much more enriched and fun your life would be.

POOR BODY IMAGE – YOU'RE NOT ALONE

If you have poor body image, the first thing to know is you are not alone. 75% of women are unhappy with their body. 50% of women who are not overweight are on a diet at any one time. This comes as no surprise, with the unrealistic body size that is promoted everywhere as the 'ideal' of what you should look like. Glamour models selling underwear for a well-known brand are typically around 5 foot 10 inches tall and have BMIs of 16 and 17, well into the anorexic spectrum. But instead of being seen as ill and emaciated they are held up as the healthy ideal to which we should all aspire.

Added to this unrealistic notion of the 'ideal', there is an unspoken message: 'If you had the discipline and put your mind to it you could look like that – so what's stopping you?' And guess what, there are lots of services and products you can buy to help you become the ideal shape and size. To make things worse, this 'ideal' is also promoted as the healthy ideal (When did emaciated become healthy?). So, if you don't want to 'put in the effort' to become beautiful, you are morally required to 'put in the effort' to be healthy. Oh, and there's a whole industry built on getting you 'healthy'. When people attempt to achieve the impossible and inevitably fail, they blame themselves for not having enough discipline, which delivers another blow to an already fragile body image. But, is discipline or your lack of discipline the problem? Let's look at what someone who has the discipline to appear on the cover of sports magazines has to say.

COMPARISON IS THE THIEF OF JOY

When it comes to body image, the bar has been set so unrealistically high that we are can all feel like failures if we compare ourselves to the pictures on Instagram. The thing to understand is that nobody looks like that, not even the models in the pictures. I am not talking about Photoshop and deceiving camera angles (although there is a lot of that about). I mean the actual models. I remember hearing a talk by a body model, let's call her Susan, who had appeared on the cover of a sports magazine. To paraphrase her, she said:

'What you've got to understand is nobody looks like that (pointing to her photo), I don't even look like that. To get that photo I had to bulk up for about 9 months, eating lots of protein, lifting heavy weights and gaining bulk. This was followed by 3 months of eating tuna and salad and doing strenuous exercise to burn off the fat. 24 hours before the shoot I dehydrated my body by sweating out the water, dropping at least 10lbs of water to get better definition on my muscles. Before the shoot I did a heavy-weight session followed by light weights to 'pump up' my muscles and we did the shoot in about 30 minutes to an hour. For that hour, I guess I looked like the photo, but for the rest of the year I didn't. I staggered out of the shoot, had a good drink of water, showered and went for the first good meal I had had in 3 months. The girl in the photo now is just a distant memory, but I got some good pics for my portfolio.'

Note the word portfolio – yes, this is Susan's full-time job.

Even if you had this amount of self-discipline and you could dedicate all your time, money and energy to your goal, you might be able to achieve a body like Susan's for one hour a year!

Let's face up to reality, you are never going to look like Susan on the cover of the sports magazine, no matter how strictly you diet, no matter what food groups you cut out or how hard you train. Even Susan can't look like that; the good news is, she has the self-awareness to know it.

HOW TO IMPROVE YOUR BODY IMAGE

Your body image is simply your opinion about how you see yourself and how you think others see you. Because it is only your personal opinion, it may or may not have any basis in reality. It's not a fact, it's just your opinion and, like any opinion, you can change it.

WE MAKE UP
OUR BODY IMAGE

The problem is that from your point of view it feels real. And you treat it as if it is real. But it's not, it's just your opinion and this can work against you and actively feed the eating disorder. To improve their body image, many people try to change the way their body looks. They go on a strict diet and an exercise regime; unfortunately, we all know how that ends. Even if you are one of the few people who is able to change their shape, this might not change the way you feel about your body, you might still have a poor body image. I know beautiful people who are professional models who have a poor body image.

A far better strategy to improve your body image is to change your opinion and develop a positive body image. At the moment, you might think it's great to know that your body image is just your opinion of how you look. But, it doesn't feel like an opinion. It feels real, so you're probably thinking what's the point in lying to yourself? However, are you sure what you are telling yourself now is correct?

Let's find out just how valid your opinion is.

Magic Weight Technique

We know how society sets unrealistic standards about how you 'should' and 'should not' look. But often we have arbitrarily set ourselves standards which are just as unrealistic. When we fail to match up to our unattainable standard, our opinion about how we look plummets. One way we do this is called your 'magic weight'. Somewhere in the back of our minds we have an ideal weight that we should be − our 'magic weight'.

A lot of people feel that they are overweight because they are heavier than some imagined idea of the weight they should be, their magic weight. It is magic because at the back of our minds, we feel that once we achieve this weight everything in our lives will be fantastic.

Take a few moments and have a think − what weight would you love to be? Once you had achieved that weight you would be happy and not worry about weight again.

What is your magic weight?

Write it here …………………………

Have you ever been that weight?	
If so, how old were you?	
How did you feel at that weight?	
How was your social life at that weight?	
Was it worth it?	

Is it still your magic weight?

The real reason it is a magic weight is because once you bring it out into the open and assess it rationally, then Abracadabra! - it disappears. While it is in the back of your mind, it makes you feel fat because you are heavier than the magic weight. Once you bring it into the daylight, you realise that it is often ridiculous and it loses its power.

MAGIC WEIGHT EXAMPLES

I recently asked the magic weight question to two people, Jemma and Peter.

Jemma is a pal who I have known for several years. She has lost around 4 stone (60lbs) and kept it off. But she is always hyper observant of what she is eating. She says that she is good at maintaining her weight but has plateaued and can't lose any more weight.

Me: Jemma, what would be your magic weight?
Immediately, Jemma answered.
Jemma: 11 stone (154lb).
Me: Have you ever been 11 stone?
Jemma: No, now that you mention it, not since I was a child.
Me: What's your weight now?
Jemma: 12 stone (168lb). I'm happy at that.

Peter is a young man with bulimia.

Me: Peter, what is your magic weight?
Immediately, Peter answered.
Peter: 9 stone (126 lbs)
Me: That would give you a BMI of 18. That's in the anorexic range.
Peter: What? I've been lighter than that.
Me: But what was it like then?
Peter: It was terrible. I was so weak, I could hardly get up for work.
Me: What was your life like then?
Peter: I didn't have one, just stayed in my bedroom and went to work.
Me: Do you still want to be 9 stone, or would you prefer to feel like you do now?
Peter: I don't want to go back there – never.

Peter abandoned his magic weight on the spot and, from then on, he was happy with gaining the weight he needed to achieve a healthy weight.

These questions helped both Jemma and Peter realise that, subconsciously, they had in their mind an unrealistic ideal body image and judged themselves against this image. Once they realised the consequences of achieving and maintaining their magic weight, they immediately abandoned it as the fantasy that it was.

Don't worry if you find out your magic weight seems silly once you uncover it. I have had clients beating themselves up because they are heavier than they were at 14. The key is that once you expose it to daylight it disappears.

We have had a look at how we can get a poor body image, how things like checking/avoiding mirrors, selfies and constant weighing etc. keep it in place and how a poor body image feeds an eating disorder. The next question is:

What do you do about it?

How do you get a better body image?

The following exercise will give you some insight as to how body image can seem much more important than it is.

Putting things into perspective technique

Take out a pad and write 'What I look for in friend' at the top of the page. Draw a line down the middle of the page and on one side

Then make a list, for example:
Trustworthy
Fair
Interesting
Funny
Friendly
Dress sense
etc.
...and so on.

Now on the other side of the line draw a rough circle and divide it up just as you would divide up a pie, but naming each section using your list. If something is very important, make the section large, and if it is not so important, make it a sliver.

WHAT I LOOK FOR IN A FRIEND.

- Trustworthy
- Fair
- Friendly
- Funny
- Dress Sense
- Lots in Common

Then at the top of a new page, write 'What do my friends like about me?' Draw a line down the middle of the page and on one side

Make a list

1.

2.

3.

4.

5.

...and so on.

Now on the other side of the line draw a rough circle and divide it up just as you did with the last one, but naming each section using your list. As before, if something is very important, make the section large, and if it is not so important, make it a sliver.

WHAT DO MY FRIENDS LIKE ABOUT ME?

- Loyal
- Funny
- Style
- Clever

At the top of a new page, write 'What is most interesting about me?' Draw a line down the middle of the page and on one side make a list.

Now on the other side of the line draw a rough circle and divide it up just as before, naming each section using your list. Again, if something is very important, make the section large, and if it is no so important, make it a sliver.

WHAT IS MOST INTERESTING
ABOUT ME

1.

2.

3.

4.

... and so on.

I am sure that there were some surprises for you as you wrote how you subconsciously felt about yourself.

How does what you think is 'most interesting about me' compare to 'what my friends like about me' and 'what I look for in a friend'? Is there some discord in the answers?

Write down the answer to 'What I learned about myself' in the box below.

This one's for you

If you are unsure what to write, the following example may help you.

Example

I did this exercise with Janet and this is what she drew:

What do you look for in a friend?

What do your friends like about you?

What do you think is interesting about you?

Janet: Hmm, that's interesting. Gosh, I seem so shallow, don't I? Do you know, I would run a mile from someone like that, so self-centred and boring. But I'm not like that – am I?

Me: No, you're nothing like that, but that's what you subconsciously think is what's important about you to others. At some level you think the most important thing about you is that you are thin. No wonder being thin has been so important to you. But, as the other diagrams show, your appearance is just a small part of what your friends like about you and not important at all in what you look for in a friend.

With that information, Janet drew a pie chart of herself in which her appearance counted for one small part, which she agreed represented her in a much more realistic way.

This exercise shows how easy it is to make our appearance seem much more important than it is. Janet was embarrassed by the amount of importance she had placed on what she considered a 'shallow' characteristic. Being thin had overshadowed her life. Being thin became so important to her, it was almost as if her value as a person depended on it. When looked at from a distance, it is obvious that this is nonsense, but it is easy to understand how we can quickly get so wrapped up with one area of our lives that it grows out of all proportion.

If you find this exercise difficult to do alone, ask someone you trust to help you with it. They will probably have a better all-round view of you.

DRAW A MORE REALISTIC PIE CHART OF YOUR CHARACTERISTICS

On another new page, make a list in answer to the question, 'Which characteristics do I most value about myself?'

As before, draw a rough circle and divide it up, naming each section using your list.

WHAT CHARACTERISTICS DO I
MOST VALUE ABOUT MYSELF

1.

2.

3.

4.

5.

...and so on.

Write down 'What is really interesting about myself' in the box below.

This one's for you

Is this second attempt a better match of the characteristics you value most about yourself? Take a good look at it and let it sink in. See yourself from this more realistic perspective. You are a whole person with lots of valuable things to offer the world and those around you – once you stop focusing on one small part of yourself. When you think of yourself, think of all the different aspects of yourself and how each can be valuable in different parts of your life and the lives of people you care about.

Gratitude Box Technique

A great way of getting things into proportion is to do some gratitude work. It is only human to take the things we have for granted and notice the things that we don't have. If we are not careful, this can give us a skewed look on life. Janet had lots of great things going on in her life, but she simply took them for granted and did not give them the value that they deserved. It's good to count your blessings now and then to put things into perspective. I find the following technique really useful.

First find a box or container and put it in a place where you can see it easily. Whenever anybody gives you a compliment, say 'thank you' and not a word more. Simply accept the compliment graciously. Many of my clients find this very difficult at first and find it somehow embarrassing. But don't worry, you will soon get the hang of it. When you get home, write the compliment down on a piece of paper and put the paper in your gratitude box. From time to time, get them out and read them. This is a really powerful thing to do, especially when times get tough.

Jars On A Shelf Technique

I once did some therapy with a woman called Jane, who was very dissatisfied with her life. All her friends seemed to be having much more exciting lives than her. Although Jane had a lot in her life when she compared it to her friends, it seemed dull and Jane thought, 'it's just not fair'. I got Jane to sit quietly and had the following conversation:

Me: Imagine all the different parts of your friend's life were put into different jars. Imagine putting all those jars on a shelf on the left side of the wall. Now imagine all the different parts of your life and put them into different jars. Put all those jars on a shelf on the right side of the wall. Now you can see both shelves on the wall: your friend's shelf on the left and your shelf on the right. Which shelf would you choose?'

Jane: My shelf, the one on the right – of course.

Me: Why?

Jane: Because I have children on my shelf and they don't on their shelf.

Me: So, you chose your life instead of theirs. How do you feel?

Jane: I suppose I feel a bit sorry for my friend missing out on having children.

We often forget that our life comes in many parts and to enjoy one part it often means giving up other parts. The secret is to recognise the point. Once Jane realised that she was not as free as her friend to do 'exciting' things because she had the greater joy of having children, she became much more satisfied with her life.

YOUR JARS

Let's look at your jars. Here are some examples to start you off. Add as many as you like.

Work	Family	Relationship
Health	Hobbies	Friendship
Home Life	Appearance	Ambition

SSSStop Technique

This is a bit more of a day to day technique which can be used to break bad habits and instill good ones.

As mentioned before, there are certain behaviours that can indicate a poor body image:

- Over checking in mirrors
- Avoiding mirrors
- Hundreds of selfies
- Avoiding being photographed
- Multiple weighing
- Pinching parts of the body
- Constantly seeking reassurance – does my bum look big in this?
- Beauty and the beast thinking – she looks beautiful, so I must look ugly
- Panicking when you feel fat
- Mind reading – everyone will think I look fat on the beach

These behaviours entrench and feed a poor body image, so stop doing them. That's right — just stop it. How do you just stop doing them? This simple but remarkably powerful technique will soon break these nasty habits.

The Ssssstop technique is simple. You might recognise this as a variant of the comedian Bob Newhart sketch, **'STOP IT'** therapy. If you are not familiar, check it out on YouTube, it's really funny. You can use this technique on any of the poor body image reinforcing behaviours.

Step one:
Catch yourself behaving in one of the ways listed – say over checking yourself in the mirror.

Step two:
Say to yourself out loud — $SSSS$ top it. Really stress the 's' in a snake-like hiss when you say Ssssstop it.

Step three:
Slowly breathe the cool air in through your nose and then slowly breathe out the warm air from your nose. Repeat until you can feel the difference between the cool air and the warm air.

Keep doing this and you will build a habit of not doing those things. I know this seems simple, but it is very powerful. Over time, you will catch yourself doing one of the behaviours, say Ssssstop it, be reminded of the Bob Newhart sketch and laugh at yourself. In my experience, once we start laughing at our little quirks, they quickly lose their power.

SOME TRICKY AREAS FOR POOR BODY IMAGE

SCALES

My particular pet hate is continual weighing. As the saying goes, 'scales belong on a fish'. Just get rid of them. What do they tell you? Nothing. Your weight can fluctuate by several pounds during the day. If you lose weight, this becomes the new bar by which to judge yourself. If you gain weight you are likely to become demotivated. Either way is triggering the very behaviour you are trying to put in your past. Scales are not helpful. Throw them away or at least hide them for a while.

Seriously though, when you weigh yourself, what are you weighing? Fluctuations in weight comprise of fluctuations in muscle, water and fat. The problem is we cannot tell which is the cause of the fluctuation. So, for example you could lose a pound of fat and retain 2lbs more water and the scale would show an increase in weight. Your clothes are a much better guide.

PHOTOGRAPHS

It's a funny thing about photographs and we have all done it. Have you ever been on holiday and seen a beautiful seascape? It just looks fantastic, so you take a photo. But when you return home and look at the photograph you are somehow disappointed. The photo looks nothing like what you remember.

When this happens to me, I usually think to myself, 'What a bad photo.'

On the other hand, we've all been at a family celebration and someone has taken a photo that is less than flattering of you. Unlike the holiday snap, I never think 'What a bad photo.' I generally think 'I look awful.' Do you see the difference? If the view didn't match the memory – it was a bad photo. When the picture of me didn't match my expectations – I look awful. It's never just a bad photo that caught me from an odd angle.

I have been fascinated by how distorting photographs can be. It is beyond the scope of this book but a quick look at photographers like Sue Bryce on YouTube will soon show you the best way to pose in photographs. A bit vain perhaps, but at least you will know how to present yourself in a good light and hopefully grow to love having your photo taken. It will also show you when a photo is taken from certain angles the result is always unflattering. Learn that it is the photographer using poor technique and not the subject that makes a bad picture.

The problem is that the camera sees the world in two dimensions, whereas we see It in three. To show the effect, hold your hands up in front of you and they look the same size. Now move one hand closer to your face – they both look the same size. This is because your brain makes allowance for perspective and you see both hands as the same size.

Now take a picture of your hands in the same positions. When you look at the photos, one hand looks much larger than the other. This is because the camera is NOT your brain and cannot make the same adjustments. The golden rule is that anything closer to the camera appears bigger and anything further away appears smaller. Subtle changes can have a massive effect, this is part of the photographer's art. In the words of the old song, 'Believe half of what you see and none of what you hear'. If you look bad in a picture, it is a bad picture or, more precisely, a bad photographer.

MIRRORS

Constantly checking in mirrors is an indicator of poor body image. But, unfortunately, it rarely adds to our confidence because where we focus magnifies. If you think you have large thighs, when you look at yourself in the mirror, your focus will be on your thighs. You will narrow your focus so that all you will notice is your 'large' thighs, because the rest of your body is out of focus. You know it's there, but you don't pay any attention to it.

One of my clients, Meg, thought she had large thighs (she didn't, by the way) and was very embarrassed by them.

Me: When you look in the mirror, what do you see?
Meg: My fat thighs.
Me: Is that all?
Meg: Yes, and I hate them.
Me: Do you know what I see when I look in the mirror?
Meg: No, what?
Me: A handsome, 30-year-old man staring back at me.
Meg: Hoots of laughter.
Me: You didn't have to laugh so loud. But it's true, when I look into a mirror I look into my eyes (where you focus magnifies) and I see a handsome, 30-year-old man looking back. Now I know how old I am, and I am not deluded, but that's what I see and I'm quite happy with that, thank you very much.

I am happy where I focus my attention, but if where you focus causes you distress, Ssssstop it. The way to do it is to first notice what you are doing and then widen your focus to see the whole of you. As your focus widens, it softens.

A good tip when you are looking at yourself in the mirror is to hold your hands out at eye level, a little wider than shoulder width in front of you. As you look in the mirror you should be able to see your hands in your peripheral vision. As your focus widens, it softens. You should be able to see all of you. Notice how seeing your hands makes things easier. It is often useful to do the nose breathing technique (breathe in the cool air and out the warm air) and relax as you look at yourself as a whole.

Keep working on your body image and you will feel so much happier in your own skin. You might never get a great body image, but it will become less and less of who you are and simply not matter as much. You might be able to say, 'I've still got fat arms, but I've got so much good stuff going on at the moment, I can't be bothered to think about it right now'.

In this chapter we looked at the effects of having a poor body image and the behaviours that indicate a poor body image. But more importantly we looked at how to improve your body image.

The key to getting a more realistic body image is to realise that we make it up. It is only our opinion of how we look, should look and look to others. With this comes the understanding that our opinion could be wrong (and probably is). So instead of trying and failing to conform to an emaciated 'ideal', a better strategy would be to improve your body image using the following techniques:

How to improve your body image

- Magic weight technique – How realistic are your unconscious weight goals?

- Putting things into perspective technique – You are more than your appearance.

- Gratitude box technique – Remember the good things about you.

- Jars on a shelf technique – There are many aspects to our lives.

- Ssssstop technique – Stop doing things that make you feel bad.

We went on to cover what to do in tricky body image areas, such as:

- Constantly checking scales – Throw them away or at least hide them.

- Constantly checking in mirrors – Sssssstop it!

- Photographs – Learning a bit about how cameras distort reality.

Remember, if you make up your body image, you might as well have a good one. Trust me, it's a lot more fun!

MY NOTES

This one's for you

WHAT I LEARNED... WHAT I WILL DO...

CHAPTER TWELVE

BULIMIA NERVOSA

This section is specifically for people who are suffering from bulimia nervosa. Bulimia nervosa, often simply described as bulimia, is defined by www.nhs.uk as:

"Bulimia is an eating disorder and mental health condition. People who have bulimia go through periods where they eat a lot of food in a very short amount of time (binge eating) and then make themselves sick, use laxatives (medication to help them poo) or do excessive exercise, or a combination of these, to try to stop themselves gaining weight. Men and women of any age can get bulimia, but it's most common in young women and typically starts in the mid to late teens."

If you are not bulimic you can skip this chapter, although you may find it can throw extra light on your condition. If you do suffer from bulimia, then it is essential that you read this section, so that you can arm yourself with knowledge about what causes and maintains your bulimia and use this knowledge to change your behaviour in a way that will form a firm basis of your recovery.

This book concentrates on your recovery, so I will not go into all the ways bulimia is bad for you. If I thought scaring you with the truth about the lives ruined and cut short by bulimia would shock you into recovery, I would do just that. But you probably already know how bulimia is bad for your health, in both the short and long term and that it can be fatal, even in young people. Instead, this chapter will give you the knowledge and skills to stop the control bulimia has over your life.

IT WON'T GET BETTER ON ITS OWN – BUT YOU CAN RECOVER

Before going further, you should know that bulimia does not tend to get better on its own. You need help to recover. I have patients who finally come to see me after they had suffered from bulimia for 10, 20 and even 30 years. They have turned it around quickly and, once they have sought help, recovered.

One of my patients, Sara wrote me this lovely testimonial:

'I booked an appointment with Tony thinking I'd tried absolutely everything. I had been battling severe bulimia for two-and-a-half years and tried but failed many times to stop. I was so desperate to change. The illness was consuming my life and having a detrimental effect on my health.

I met with Tony and after my first appointment realised he understood more than my counsellor had managed to understand in a year. He taught me so much about the illness that had taken over my life and helped me realise for the first time that I could beat this.

After my second session I was able to control the voice that had consumed my life for so long and I finally felt like I had my own voice coming back.

For someone who hadn't managed more than 2 days without a bulimia cycle in two-and-a-half years, after my second session I'm amazed at how I've managed to control the urge and got into a pattern of regular eating.

Tony's support has been amazing, and I can't put into words how he has not only given me the tools to fix my problem he's given me the realisation that I finally can have my life back and can beat this FOREVER.'

In this chapter I will run through what I do with my clients, including Sara, to help them.

FIRST STEP TO RECOVERY

Take a deep breath, because the first step in recovery is to make a promise to yourself, that from this point on, no matter what happens, you are not going to purge. I know… if only it was that easy. But the fact of the matter is that while purging is still an option, bingeing will always be more tempting. Stick with me on this, and once you have a true understanding about the effect of purging on your body, you will see that it is pointless and does not achieve what you think it will achieve. It just feeds your eating disorder and gets in the way of your recovery.

To help you, it might be useful to bust some of the myths around bulimia. Most of my clients first started to purge in an attempt to lose weight and it is this belief, that bulimia helps them lose weight keeps them locked firmly in bulimic behaviour. My clients come to me wanting to recover for lots of reasons (I'm sure you have a few yourself). But there is always an underlying assumption – 'purging keeps my weight down.' But does it? The question they never seem to ask is 'Does purging work?' Is it effective in keeping their weight down? Well I think if you haven't already, it is time you asked yourself that question and got some solid answers.

DOES BULIMIA WORK? DOES IT HELP YOU LOSE WEIGHT?

People diet with one thought in mind – to lose weight. Unfortunately, for them the body does not realise this is the intention and interprets the lack of food as a period of famine and goes into survival mode. In survival mode, the body reacts in a number of ways, but the outcome is usually the same. People stick to their diet for so long and then they lapse and break one of their many diet rules, followed by 'I've blown it', followed by a binge, which is usually followed by further restriction which leads to a further binge and so the downward spiral begins.

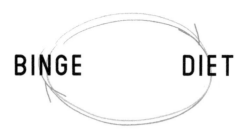

BINGE   DIET

At first sight, bulimia seems to solve the problem of bingeing. People with bulimia are trying to lose weight, so they restrict what they eat. As before, the body responds to the lack of food by going into survival mode, which usually results in a binge. But by purging, people with bulimia think (wrongly) that there is no consequence to bingeing and so, after the purge, think they have solved the problem and start to restrict again.

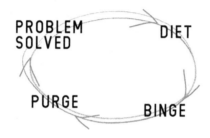

PROBLEM   DIET
SOLVED

PURGE   BINGE

But unfortunately, as with most things,

'It's a bit more complicated than that.'

Like dieting, bulimia seems to work in the short term, but the body soon responds in all sorts of ways and the weight goes back on and often more so. As a way of losing weight, bulimia does not work.

You might be thinking, 'Of course it works; if a person purges, surely they won't get fat.'

Well, you might think that, and it sounds reasonable, but you would be wrong. Ask yourself this: 'If bulimia worked, why aren't all bulimics stick thin?' In fact, most bulimics are normal weight or overweight. Just let that sink in.

In fact, bulimia actually makes weight loss much more difficult.

'But Tony,' you might say, 'if it doesn't work, why do people persist in doing it for years?' That is a very good question. Ironically, people get locked into bulimia, BECAUSE it does not work.

THE BULIMIA TRAP

One of the main reasons people persist in bulimia, although it does not work, is the fear that they will get fat if they stop (vomiting, laxative abuse, over exercising). It starts off quite innocuously; at first a person starts of thinking that purging solves the problem of bingeing. But they soon find themselves in an increasingly desperate trap.

STAGE 1

'I am trying to lose weight. I am good at sticking to my diet, but every now and again I break down and binge. I purge to make up for the binge. Problem solved.'

But this soon changes to Phew – I'm still losing weight.

STAGE 2

'I am trying to lose weight. I am good at sticking to my diet, but I keep breaking down and bingeing. I purge to make up for the binge. I'm not losing weight but at least I'm not gaining weight from the binge.'

And finally:

STAGE 3

'I am trying to lose weight. I am good at sticking to my diet, but I keep bingeing. I purge to make up for the binges. Even though I'm purging, I'm gaining weight – just think how fat I would be if I didn't purge!'

So, the less the bulimia works, the less it helps you lose weight, the more dependent you become and the more completely it takes over your life.

PURGING MAKES WEIGHT LOSS MORE DIFFICULT

People with bulimia think they have found a way of 'having their cake and eating it'. But have they? Well, unfortunately no. In fact, bulimia makes bingeing worse in 3 main ways:

1. People who purge binge more often.
2. People who purge have bigger binges.
3. Purging simply does NOT work.

PEOPLE WITH BULIMIA BINGE MORE OFTEN

For a start, people with bulimia are more likely to binge than people who only binge eat. Binge eaters find themselves bingeing out of control. They may feel good during the binge, but once the euphoria has passed, they have to face the consequences of their behaviour.

Whereas people with bulimia feel the euphoria of the binge, but by purging feel that the binge has no consequences and so it is no big deal. Why not eat what they want and then get rid of it? Because, they think there are no consequences to bingeing in the form of weight gain, people with bulimia tend to binge more often.

PEOPLE WITH BULIMIA HAVE BIGGER BINGES

Bulimia encourages bigger binges; many bulimics turn mild overeating into a full-scale binge to make it worth the discomfort of vomiting.

If you are going to all the trouble of forcing your body to vomit and to clean up after yourself, it's got to be worth it. So, when a person with bulimia has a 'slip' and breaks one of their many strict food rules, they know that they will feel compelled to purge. So instead of saying to themselves, 'That was just a slip,' and forget about it, they think to themselves, 'I've blown it, I might as well be hung for a sheep as a lamb. Might as well make it worth it.' The slip turns into a full-blown binge to make it worth the hassle. 'What's the harm?' they reason, 'I'll get rid of it all and cut back tomorrow.'

People with bulimia are much more likely to turn a 'slip' into a binge and have bigger binges because they think they have got away with eating the extra calories. But have they?

PURGING DOES NOT WORK

Purging in bulimia takes 3 main forms: laxative abuse, over-exercising and vomiting. I think you already know the answer, but let's look at each of these in turn to see if they work.

LAXATIVES

Where do I begin? Laxative abuse is extremely painful, it has long term health consequences and it DOES NOT work. Most food is digested in the small intestine, before what is left is passed to the large intestine. But laxatives only work on the large intestine, by which time over 90% of what will be digested has already been digested.

Yes, you feel thinner, but basically you have gone through considerable pain (and the pain can be agonizing) to simply lose water. Water that will be re-absorbed with your next drink.

I won't go into the numerous, often long-term damaging effects of abusing laxatives (which are horrendous). But as a way of compensating for a binge, it is completely useless.

OVER-EXERCISING

This is a variation on the 'calories in, calories out' myth. 'Oh no!' you've had a binge – no problem, just go for a run in the morning and work it off.

But is this realistic? If you have a small binge, say 1000 calories, you will have to run around 16 miles at 5mph to burn that off – that's well over a half marathon. Do you really have over 3 hours for that run in the morning? Face it, it's not going to happen and a quick trot round the block won't even scratch the surface.

Oh, by the way, the average binge is around 3000 calories. I'll let you do the maths.

VOMITING

You might concede that laxatives and exercising are worse than useless for getting rid of the extra calories from a binge. But surely, vomiting works. You can't digest food that's not in your body.

You might think that, but you would be wrong. When you binge, you usually eat lots of foods that are rapidly digested (sweet fatty food). A large amount of this food is digested even before you've finished eating. So even if you purge immediately after bingeing, a lot of the food is already digested. After vomiting, around 1200 calories – the equivalent of 2 large meals – are absorbed by the body. Far from a method of losing weight, bulimia is a great way of gaining weight.

A better weight control method would be to eat a really nice meal of around 600 calories, rather than a round of bingeing and purging and gaining 1200 calories. I know which I think is more fun.

TO SUM UP:

- People who purge are more likely to binge
- People who purge have bigger binges.
- With each binge, even after purging, the body retains and digests approximately 1200 extra calories (the equivalent of 2 large meals).

Bulimia does not help you lose weight. In fact, it makes weight loss more difficult and weight gain is very common.

Now that you understand that purging is getting in the way of your recovery, make a pact to stop purging now. It is doing nothing for you

PURGE PREVENTION

The best way to prevent purging is to prevent bingeing. If you lapse and have a binge, don't further entrench your purging habit. Stop and remember there is no rush. Take it easy and do one of your self-soothing techniques and calm down. Once you are calm, ask yourself:

Is there something that I can learn from this?

Have a think about what was happening before the binge.

Check to see if this is the case.

Look at your diary and see if you have:

- been eating as planned – 3 meals and 3 snacks?
- eaten roughly balanced meals?
- missed a meal?
- gone a long time between eating?
- been restricting?
- checked your hunger levels?

Most of the time your diary will show you what caused the binge. Your diary will give you feedback so you can identify the cause and then make the changes to make sure it doesn't happen again. Top tip: it's usually low blood sugar levels.

If you only do one thing when you get up in the morning – remember to eat your breakfast.

BITESIZE

You are aware of the basic facts about bulimia:

- We discussed the 'Bulimia trap' – paradoxically, the less the bulimia works (in terms of weight loss) the stronger and more controlling the bulimia becomes.

- Purging makes weight loss more difficult in that people with bulimia tend to:

  o have more binges.
  o have bigger binges.

- Laxatives and exercise are useless in compensating for the binge.

- Exercise does not get rid of the extra calories.

- Vomiting does not work and around 1200 calories are digested.

In short, bulimia DOES NOT work and makes weight gain more likely.

The first step to recovery is to make a commitment to yourself that you will never purge again. This seems a lot to ask but now you know a lot more about your condition it will become considerably easier.

MY NOTES

This one's for you

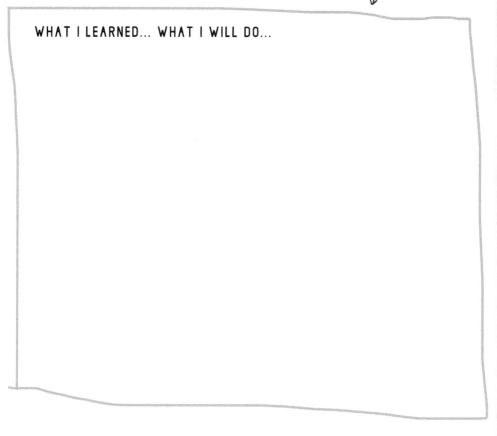

WHAT I LEARNED... WHAT I WILL DO...

SECTION THREE

LIVING IN RECOVERY

CHAPTER THIRTEEN

RELAPSE PREVENTION

By now you have the knowledge and techniques that you need to recover from bulimia and binge eating. I know that it is a lot to take in and you may want to return to certain parts of the book from time to time. That's fine, that's how we learn.

You have read that restricting your body by dieting, for whatever reason, sets in motion a survival reaction in the body. This survival reaction has a two-pronged approach. Firstly, it reduces the quantity of calories your body needs to function by reducing your metabolism (your body simply stops doing non-essential processes and reduces essential processes to a minimum), making it much harder to lose weight and results in your body holding on to fat and breaking down your own muscles to provide protein for your body (not a good thing). Secondly, like any starving animal, food becomes the number one priority. Your mind becomes obsessed by food and the smell and taste of food becomes irresistible. It is no wonder that under such strong pressure bingeing becomes almost inevitable. In many ways, it is the natural response to hunger. This response to hunger has enabled us, as a species, to survive famines over thousands of years and we should not be surprised when it happens.

You also know how your eating disorder draws energy from what you think and what you do. More importantly, you now have the knowledge and skills to change what you think and what you do, reducing the stress and anxiety that feeds your eating disorder, thereby reducing its strength until it just fades away.

You have learned how to:

- end food chaos by stabilising your blood sugar levels
- set yourself up for success
- use skills and techniques to:
- shut up the critical voice
- reduce perfectionist tendencies
- challenge black and white thinking
- handle emotions
- get a realistic body image

You know how to work with your body by feeding it nourishing food regularly throughout the day and how to use tools like the Food and Mood Diary to find out what works for your body. So now all you have to do is to do it. Scary or what!

You may already have started and just taken to it naturally. I find with many of my clients that a light goes on and they never look back. But for most people, lapses are a normal part of the process that leads to recovery.

This chapter will help you to put any lapse into perspective and show you how to bounce back quickly.

But what if I fail?

It's natural to worry. After all, you have been haunted by this condition which has taken up so much of your life. You have read this book which explains how to recover, and it seems to make sense – but what if it doesn't work for you at first go? That critical voice will be telling you the hundred and one reasons why it won't work for you and that is a scary place to be. So, let's look at it head on. Recognise your perfectionist tendencies are probably at play and lighten up. This is not an event where you can win or lose, it is a process where you might go off track now and again (and you will go off track now and again). Every time you go off track, use your diary and see what it has to teach you about what works and what doesn't work for your body and learn from it. The only way to fail in a learning process is to stop trying.

It's a bit like riding a bike; think back to how difficult it was. But did you get on the bike for the first time, fall off and think, 'That's it, I've failed' and never try again?' No, you got help. You got stabilisers, so you could learn all the skills to ride a bike while the stabilisers helped you to balance. Later, you could remove one of the stabilisers, then both, and finally you could ride the bike. But no matter how wobbly you rode that first 5 yards, you knew deep inside it was only a matter of time before you could ride the bike anywhere you liked, without thinking about it. OK, so if you did try once, fell off and never got on a bike again, maybe this isn't the best metaphor for you, but I am sure you can think of something which didn't work first time but your persistence eventually paid off: learning to play the piano, understanding fractions, tying your shoelaces or cooking a soufflé!

As I'm writing this, I am thinking about how apt the riding a bike metaphor is for recovery. There is an old English saying: 'It's just like riding a bike'. Once you learn something like riding a bike, you learn it deeply, at a subconscious level and that never leaves you. So, for example, you could learn to ride a bike as a child but, once learned, if you didn't ride a bike for 10 or 20 years, somehow your body would still know how, and you would trust it to get on with the task. This is what I want for you. I want you to use this book as a type of stabiliser while you are recovering, but I want you to pass rapidly through this stage so you can take your stabilisers off and leave it to your body to get on with keeping you in balance.

Lapses are part of the process of change

With any change there is always a chance of a lapse. So, if that happens you can use 'Setting yourself up for success' (that you read in Chapter 7: Setting yourself up for success) to turn lapses into learning experiences. That's great in theory, but sometimes we need a little time between having a lapse and trying to learn from what went wrong. At the time there is often a lot of anxiety and you need a way to rapidly self-soothe, reduce the anxiety and cut yourself a little slack. The problem is that when we are anxious, we are not in the best place to decide the best way forward. So, it is always a good idea to draw up a self-soothing plan.

My self-soothing plan

This is simple list of the things that help to reduce anxiety. We all have ways of calming down, and these can be very personal, so it is worth making a list of what works for you. Here are a few examples, but the more personal your list, the better.

Write your own personal self-soothing plan here.

If I have a lapse I will:
1. Go for a walk

2. Phone my friends and catch-up
3. Have a bath
4. Listen to music

Put it in a notebook you carry or, better still, on your phone so that it is handy whenever you might need it. When you feel anxious, simply look at the list and do one of the activities.

My relapse prevention plan

In a similar way, it is a good idea to write down what you will do if you find yourself slipping back into old habits or unhelpful ways of thinking. This acts as an early warning system.

As before, you will need to write your personal list. Here are some examples:

If I find myself doing...	I will do this...
Thinking about going on a diet	re-read section on food knowledge
Thinking about losing weight before a wedding, holiday, event	read that dieting doesn't work and this will set me up for the binge purge cycle that will inevitably happen
Doing checking behaviour	Ssssstop technique
The voice is getting louder	Practise the 'You are not the voice technique'
I don't want to go to a party because of how I look	Do the 'what do my friends like about me' pie chart. Think that if I don't go they will miss all these parts of me that they find so interesting.

	Stop catastrophising. Ask myself 'what's the worst thing that can happen?' Set some boundaries If I have been invited it would be rude not to go. Make a deal with myself. I have been invited so I will go. I will have a first drink and chat to the host and stay for the buffet. After the buffet I can then make a decision whether to stay or go home.
I feel like I really need to exercise	Do I want to exercise? If I feel I NEED to exercise, think again. To decide, ask myself 'If I knew that no matter how much exercise I did it would not burn any calories, would I still want to do it?' Hmmm. Do a self-soothing technique.

MY PERSONAL PLAN

You know yourself better than anyone, so write a list of the things that will warn you that you are slipping into old habits. Then write a list of what you would do to recover, what you know will work for you.

If I find myself doing...	I will do this...

This will help you identify old habits quickly. The sooner they are spotted, the easier it is to get back on track. Finally, if you do make a choice that you regret, try the kindness technique.

Kindness Technique

The key to the Kindness Technique is to remember the goal is 'improvement not perfection'. If you keep improving, you will eventually get to your goal and recover. I got this technique from Kelly Clark, eating disorder recovery coach and author of *It Took Me 10 Years to Lose 10 Pounds* from: the10principles.com

The Kindness Technique is probably doing the opposite to what you have been doing in the past. You know that whenever you had a lapse in the past it inevitably led to a binge (last supper) followed by a new start the next morning with renewed motivation to be more disciplined this time. Unfortunately, you know how that story ends. In some way you are punishing yourself for not sticking to your diet and 'naughty boys and girls' need to be punished, or they will never learn. Instead of repeating this destructive habit, I urge you to ask yourself, 'Did it work?' Did punishing yourself ever work? You know it never does; if it did you would not have a problem and you wouldn't be reading this book. There is an old saying in the therapy world:

'If you always do what you've always done, you always get what you always got.'

You probably have years of experience of what doesn't work. Let's try something different. Instead of punishing your lapses, try The Kindness Technique.

If you look to a point in the future where you have achieved your goal, you can imagine a straight line like an arrow going through time to your goal.

NOW ————————————————→ GOAL

So, you draw up a plan and set off. Suddenly, you have a lapse and deviate from the path to your goal.

NOW → GOAL

What do you do? In the past you probably thought 'I need to make up for that lapse, cut back on food and hit the gym'. **STOP!** You know how that ends – spiraling down in that same old self destructive pattern that gets you nowhere. Before you do anything, get out your self-soothing plan and put into motion *The Kindness Technique*.

1. SELF-SOOTHE

Pull out your Self-Soothing Plan and do one of the things on the list. Then, once the anxiety has drained from the situation, continue with the next steps.

2. DETACH

Think about what happened and, when you do, practise the See Yourself quotes around See Yourself in The Image Technique (page 139) and detach yourself from the event. Often when we use the technique, when we remember events and see ourselves in the image, we feel a little sorry for the person in the image. This separation lets you see how hard you have been trying and how upset you are and you realise you need kindness not punishment, so you can put the incident into perspective. 'So, what? I ate a piece of cake.'

3. DO WHAT WORKS

Ask yourself this Power Question: 'What is the one thing I can do now that will get me closer to my goal?' Well, your experience has shown you it might feel good to punish yourself, remove a bit of guilt, but in reality, it will set you up for yet another restrict-purge-cycle which will take you further away from your goal. If you keep doing things that get you closer to your goal, eventually you will get there.

Instead, go back to the basics that you know work (from your Food and Mood Diary). For example, if you have over-eaten one night, ask yourself the power question, 'What is the one thing I can do now that will get me closer to my goal?'. The answer is to eat your breakfast, stabilise your blood sugar levels using structured eating and push on towards your goal.

4. LEARNING EXPERIENCE

Finally, once you are calm and feeling kind to yourself, use your detachment to turn this lapse into a learning experience so you don't make the same mistake again. Try to find out what caused you to make that choice you later regretted and put in place some alternatives so you don't fall into the same trap twice. Look in your Food and Mood Diary and see if you had been eating regularly before the slip. If not, start to eat in a structured way – this will get you closer to your goal. If you have not been keeping your Food and Mood Diary, start keeping it again – this will get you closer to your goal.

When you make a choice that you later regret, develop the habit of doing what you know works for you. Don't waste your time wallowing in what happened. That's in the past and we can't change the past. Don't waste your energy on things that you can't change. Develop a positive habit by saying to yourself, 'What can I do now to get me closer to my goal?' then do it. With every small step, you are getting nearer and nearer to your goal.

During recovery, many people understandably have a fear of failing, yet again. But, recovery is not a pass/fail situation. Recovery is not an event but a process, and lapses are to be expected; they are part of the process. Given that lapses are part of the process, the question is 'what do you do about them?'

The first thing is to set up a Self-Soothing Plan so that you can quickly bounce back from lapses when they happen.

The next step is to set up an early warning system in the form of a Relapse Prevention Plan. Don't wait until it happens. Identify thoughts and behaviours that indicate you are slipping into old unhelpful habits and intervene before they get deeply entrenched.

Finally, if you find yourself doing something that you later regret, use the Kindness Technique to get you closer to your goal.

THE KEY TO RECOVERY IS:

IMPROVEMENT
NOT
PERFECTION

MY NOTES

This one's for you

WHAT I LEARNED... WHAT I WILL DO...

CHAPTER FOURTEEN

HOW TO HELP FRIENDS AND RELATIVES

You may have picked this book up because you are worried about a friend or relative and have no idea what to do to help them. The first thing I will say is how nice it is that you care so much that you want to help them. I hope that the book has helped you to understand their situation a bit better. However, I also want to make clear that unless they are willing to make the commitment to change, it isn't going to work, you can't do it for them. That said, if you are concerned for someone (friend, loved one or child) with an eating disorder, here are some suggestions of how you can help them. For the sake of clarity, in this chapter I will refer to the person you are trying to help as your friend.

PARENTS – 'IT'S PROBABLY NOT YOUR FAULT.'

Whatever your child tells you, it's probably NOT your fault. Stop feeling guilty, it doesn't help anybody, least of all your child.

This seems a strange, because if you ask people with eating disorders 'When did food first become a problem to you?', many will point to a certain day when they were quite young and somebody made a passing remark which they can vividly remember to the present day. You know the kind of thing: 'Oh, look at those chubby cheeks!' etc. The thing is, you could have said the same remark to 100 children and 99 will have paid little or no attention to it. But people with eating disorders tend to be very sensitive and passing remarks can often go in deep and really hurt. But you can't legislate for that, you cannot be walking on eggshells the whole of your life. What you can do, if you come across a sensitive soul, is respect their nature and try not to be cruel. They are not being silly or attention seeking, it's just that some people are easily hurt.

But at the same time, you can't just sit back and watch your child suffer. In the following section I talk about helping a friend, and this advice will also help you support your child.

HOW YOU CAN HELP YOUR FRIEND

The first thing you can do is to get a good understanding of the problem. This book will give you a basic grounding in what causes the eating disorder, how it is maintained and the steps your friend will need to make to recover. Please encourage them to read the book and support them to change. While you are supporting them, be prepared to make changes yourself, because some of the issues discussed here can be applied generally to life's challenges.

HOW TO TALK TO PEOPLE WITH EATING DISORDERS

I am from an academic background and I like nothing better than an academic discussion, logically defending your own argument and attacking your opponent's standpoint. This is exactly what NOT to do when talking to your friend with an eating disorder. It will not change their behaviour, but will make them feel defensive and will further undermine their confidence. You might win the argument, but nothing will change.

Key to this is knowing your friend is not being silly, willful, attention-seeking or mad. Your friend is in a state of abject fear, not a bit scared, but in the throes of a full-blown physical fear response. They are in the fight, flight or freeze mode and no amount of good arguments or suggestions are going to take the fear away. Your role is to reduce the fearful emotions and offer support to make change possible. Don't worry, there are some well-established ways of doing just that.

A WORD OF WARNING

When we see someone we care about suffering, it is natural for us to sympathise with them and feel their pain and anguish. But if you want to help them to recover, it is important that you do not become immersed in their suffering. If you do, it will be very uncomfortable for you, but more importantly, while you are feeling their anguish you will be too distressed to help them. In fact, you will probably make them feel even worse by legitimising how they feel.

I know this can seem a little cold, but to help them you need to step back a little emotionally (heart). This way you will be able to understand what they are going through while having a little distance (head) to support them to recover. Use some of the distancing techniques outlined earlier in the book to help you shield yourself from absorbing their emotions.

It sounds harsh, but you feeling bad will not help your loved one to recover.

DO'S AND DON'TS

Eating disorders can be quite sensitive subjects, often accompanied by shame and other negative emotions. Remind your friend that their eating disorder is an illness, like any other illness. It is not a personal failing.

Learn as much as you can about eating disorders from credible sources (there is a list of useful sources of information at the back of this book). This will give you a firm foundation from which you can help your friend. You will be able to challenge any myths they hold and rules they have around food and exercise (and they will have plenty) from a firm knowledge base. Reading this book, for example, is a good start.

Avoid making over simplistic statements such as 'Why don't you just stop purging?' or 'All you've got to do is stop eating when you are full.' If your friend could, they would have probably done it years ago. It just makes them feel worse and convinces them that you don't understand what they are going through.

USE 'I' STATEMENTS

Reduce emotions by the words you use. Instead, use 'I' statements. Simply starting statements with the word 'you' can seem like an accusation and will put people on the defensive. For example, if you say, 'You have eaten plenty already, you should be full,' This will raise their hackles and, before you know it, you will be in an emotionally charged argument. Whereas if you start a sentence with 'I' it doesn't seem so much of an accusation. For example, you could rephrase the earlier remark as 'I have noticed that you have been eating quite a lot and I am concerned that you might be finding it hard to stop eating.' This somehow takes the emotion out of the situation and your friend might be more inclined to open up and discuss their problem.

Reduce emotions by sticking to the facts. Just say what you have seen. Instead of saying 'I think you are going to the bathroom between each course in the meal to throw up'. Stick to the facts and say, 'I have noticed that you go to the bathroom between each course of the meal. I am concerned that you might be making yourself sick.'

Know your limitations. With the best will in the world, you have not had professional training and can only help your friend so much. Encourage them to get professional help and support them in their recovery.

BE PREPARED FOR A NEGATIVE REACTION

Whereas most people with an eating disorder, at some level, will be glad of your concern, some might respond by downplaying the problems and the risks involved and others might push back and will tell you to mind your own business. As before, don't get into a debate. Simply reiterate your concern and say that you are there to support them.

Don't offer solutions to their problem. Your solutions will be met with resistance and will be counterproductive. Remember, your friend has been trapped in a behaviour that they hate, and they have had plenty of time to work out their excuses. They will have a reason why they carry on doing what they do and why anything you can come up with 'will not work'.

Eating disorders have nothing to do with reason and logic. There is no good reason and it is logically self-defeating, but that doesn't stop your friend suffering. Be careful because it is easy for you to get sucked into a circular argument with them. They tell you how awful it is for them, you come up with a solution and they counter with 'yes, but…' and give you lots of reasons why it won't work for them. You then come up with a further solution and you go round and round until you both agree how awful it is for them. I know you really want to help, but getting sucked into a cycle of 'Isn't it awful… Have you tried? Yes, but… Isn't it awful' solves nothing.

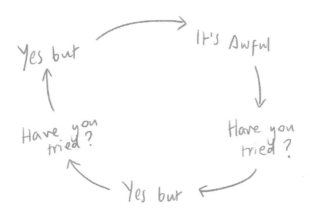

YOUR ROLE

What you can do is to become the safe, calm, wise person that they can depend on. If they start to get a bit wobbly and have a lapse and come to you for support, sit calmly with them and let them tell you what happened. Then use the Kindness Technique and say, 'I can see you are upset, and I understand why. What is the one thing you could do now to get you closer to your goal?' This is a power question and it is important to get the wording right. Do not disempower them by asking what you can do to help them. Simply let them come up with the answer and help them to do it. It might be as simple as eating their breakfast or keeping their diary up to date. It really doesn't matter, as long as it is a positive act of kindness that gets them nearer to their goal and breaks the negative cycle of bingeing and purging.

LET THEM FEEL THE CONSEQUENCES OF THEIR ACTIONS

A big part of recovery is about understanding the consequences of what we do. We are all individuals, and everyone has to learn this at their own pace. So, if your friend says, 'but I can't eat in the morning', say OK and let them feel the consequences of their actions. Check in later and say, 'you didn't eat breakfast today, how was the rest of your day?' When they tell you the knock-on effects (the consequences of not eating breakfast), say, 'So you didn't eat breakfast today, and the knock-on effects were ...' Whatever you say, do NOT say 'I told you so.' Let them arrive at their own conclusions. This will give you a little distance. It is difficult for you to feel sorry for someone who is suffering because they won't do a simple thing, like eat breakfast. This distance puts the responsibility for their suffering back with them. They are not suffering because of some awful thing that happens to them. They can stop it anytime they want to. All they have to do is to eat breakfast.

Try not to get frustrated. When you realise that when your friend says, 'I can't eat breakfast', they are in effect saying, 'I'm afraid to eat breakfast'. Keep letting them feel the consequences of not eating breakfast and dispassionately point out the facts that you see. For example, 'I notice you didn't eat breakfast and you have been in a bad temper all morning.'

BATTLEFIELD AVOIDANCE

Try not to get drawn into an argument. Whatever your friend says (and it can get nasty), simply restate your original observation – 'I notice you didn't eat breakfast and you have been in a bad temper all morning' – and leave it at that. The combination of their feeling awful and you pointing out the cause (and implying the solution to their discomfort) will allow them to come around, sooner or later. Keep in mind that once they start eating breakfast and feel the positive consequences, they will soon start to love eating breakfast.

One final word: good luck in helping your friend. You will need to develop a shield around yourself so that you don't allow their pain and suffering to affect you. Some of the distancing techniques earlier in the book can be very helpful to you. Always bear in mind that your friend may need independent professional help and you can encourage them to get the help they need.

BITESIZE

If you are supporting a friend or loved one with an eating disorder, you are in for a difficult but rewarding journey. Along the way, you will learn a great deal both about your loved one and also about yourself. That said, supporting somebody with an eating disorder is not for the fainthearted so arm yourself with knowledge and you will not only save yourself a lot of heartache, but more importantly be more effective in helping your loved one to recover.

Your role is to become the safe, calm, wise person that they can depend on.

- Your first step is to learn as much about the condition as you can. This book is a good start, and I have provided lots of resources in Chapter 17: Resources that will help you. These knowledgeable writers have the talent to be able to communicate complex topics in a practical, no nonsense way.

- Don't get dragged into the blame game; in the vast majority of cases it is simply NOT your fault and feeling guilty will not help your loved one to recover.

- Don't get into a debate, they know it's not rational at a certain level – 'proving' it's not rational to them will not change a thing.

- Don't offer simplistic solutions like 'why don't you just stop eating when you have had enough'.

- Don't state your opinion (no matter how right you are), simply stick to the facts and use 'I' statements such as, 'I noticed that you have eaten a lot and I am concerned that you are finding it hard to stop.'

- Be prepared for rejection and don't take it personally, it is simply the eating disorder lashing out. It wants your loved one to be isolated from 'interference' from you so it can get on with further embedding the disorder. Your job is to recognise this and simply be there as the safe, calm person they can depend on.

- Let them feel the consequences of their behaviour.

- Be patient and be there to help them get back up when they fall.

Good luck. You have taken on a very difficult role. Use the techniques in this book to protect yourself as you help your loved one. But when they recover, they will repay you a thousand-fold by blossoming into their old true self again.

MY NOTES

This one's for you

WHAT I LEARNED... WHAT I WILL DO...

CHAPTER FIFTEEN

REAL WORLD PROBLEMS

Once you have fully recovered, you can make a key decision. Some people just want to put it all behind them and get on with their lives. Considering the exhausting effects of eating disorders, it is understandable if you don't want to spend another second on them. Others are appalled by the consequences of diet culture and want to help with the fight against it. Both options are fine – but, and this is a big but, if you chose the second option, make sure you are **FULLY RECOVERED FIRST** before deciding.

That said, you are going to encounter some difficult situations as you recover. I believe in the concept of pre-warned is pre-armed, so here is the heads-up about some difficult situations that many of my clients have encountered and how they overcame them.

DIET 'EXPERTS'

We all have friends who are totally wrapped up with how they look, their exercise programme and the latest diet. Well, that's OK for them, if they like to play at dieting and exercising, but it's not OK for you. When I said the words 'play at dieting', did it make you pause for thought? I know that YOU don't play at dieting; for you it is a serious business. But this is not the case for a lot of people, it's a kind of game that they play to convince themselves that they are being healthy. They have a detox one week and eat junk food for the rest of the month. Now, that is NOT how you go about things, and this is why you can't get involved in these conversations. If friends try to get you to go on a diet or a 'challenge' with them, simply say these words:

'You go on a diet if you want to, but I tend to take these things far too seriously and can easily get obsessed by them – and it NEVER ends well'.

Leave it at that and don't try to explain. Most people will take the hint, and if they don't, simply repeat the sentence again and stick to it. If it makes them feel better, that's up to them. Say to yourself 'whatever' and let them get on with their games. Remember, it's just a game to them and you don't have to play.

I know it is difficult not to try to help your friends, but at this point in time, your recovery is your priority. It's worth remembering, by reading this book and putting it into practice, you have learned a lot: you know how to work with your body, you understand what your body needs to work efficiently and healthily, and you have learned the skills you will need to build positive habits that will put your eating disorder firmly in the past. Unfortunately, the majority of your friends, colleagues and relations have not. Most of these people have spent lots of money, time and energy trying to live up to the impossible demands of diet culture. They are not about to change, and it is NOT your job to convince them that they have been lied to. Your job is to concentrate on recovering fully from your eating disorder. Pointless arguments with people still in diet culture will not help you achieve your goal and might even destabilise it.

When people start going on about the latest great diet / exercise regime, just try to change the subject if this fails, I tell my clients:

"Look down and check - are your feet nailed to the floor? If not, you do not have to stand there and listen to this stuff yet again."

Pop to the bathroom and hopefully they will have moved on to something interesting when you get back.

OLD THINKING BUBBLES UP

From time to time you will be happily going along, when almost without realising it, your old eating disorder thinking starts up. Something triggers the habit and, before you know it, you are planning a binge. This is normal, but now you have choices about what to do.

One of my clients, Jean, found out her trigger was when she was tired out and felt put-upon. After months of being binge- and purge-free, she suddenly found herself planning a binge/purge. This is what she told me and how she dealt with it with what she had learned:

'I think something has moved in my head. Last week I had a very busy day, and when I came home about 7:00pm and my daughters wanted a lift to see a film. It was a long drive and it wasn't worth driving home, so I had to wait around for about 2 hours or so for them. I was at a low ebb, I had been rushed off my feet all day and now this. All I wanted to do was relax with my feet p and now it would be almost 10:00pm before I go lome. I was tired, grumpy and feeling sorry for myself when I saw a KFC and I thought 'why not? I can get rid of it when I get home.' Well, I went nd ordered a meal & ate it - It must've been year. ince I had eaten a KFC. I felt a lot better, and when I picked the girls up, we all had a laugh oing home as they talked about the film. When got home, I thought to myself 'Naw, you don't ave to do that anymore.' I realised that I had een simply hungry and didn't bother to purge, I just forgot about it. That would have not happened before - something has definately shifte in my thinking. It told me I'm not going back now.'

HOW TO SURVIVE THE WEDDING BUFFET (OR ANY BUFFET!)

We've all been there and every time it comes as such a surprise. You've been invited to a wedding or some special occasion. You might even have gone on a diet beforehand to look good in your wedding outfit and now you find yourself waiting in line at the buffet. Suddenly, you start to feel impatient: 'What's taking so long?' The buffet was supposed to be at 8 and it's 8:30pm already and a long line of people are waiting between you and the buffet. 'What are those people doing?' The queue doesn't seem to be getting shorter. You start to wonder if there will be enough food left. The people in front seem to be taking ages, stopping at each pile of food and slowly deciding whether to eat something or not and you suddenly realise that you are starving and really need to eat and to eat NOW.

Slowly, the queue moves forward and you see the food. There seems to be plenty: lots of sandwiches and rolls with various fillings – ham, beef, and egg salad – pork pies, samosas, onion bhajis, spring rolls, chicken legs, bowls of potato crisps and a big bowl of chips (fries if you are American). Oh yes, there is a small bowl of salad and some cold pasta salad and beyond them are the desserts: gateaux, chocolate cake, lots of smaller individual cakes and a large jug of cream. Oh look, there's cheese and biscuits for those without a sweet tooth. You know what happens next? Why does it always happen?

The Plan
You think to yourself, 'I'm only going to eat what I will really enjoy.' You tick off that you would like a ham sandwich, a chicken leg and a piece of pork pie and some salad. You can decide on dessert later if you are still hungry.

The Reality
That's the plan, but somehow you find yourself eating crisps while you are still waiting in line, along with a ham sandwich, and all the time you are eyeing up the chips, wondering if they will be enough, or maybe they will bring some more freshly fried chips by the time you get there.

Finally, you go back to your seat and look at your plate; somehow you have managed to fit 3 sandwiches, 2 chicken legs, 3 spring rolls and 3 pork pies, along with a small mountain of chips, on your plate. You begin to wonder what happened. But not for long, as you concentrate on eating, faster than normal and wondering if there will be enough for seconds.

There is, and you eat a second plate of food: 'It would be a shame to waste all that food.' Shortly after, you realise you have demolished 2 plates groaning with food, 2 portions of cake with cream and are presently finishing off your cheese and biscuits. How did that happen? You have no idea, but your waistband is straining and you are feeling slightly sick – again. What is up with you?

Well the answer is there is nothing is wrong with you. It's not you, it's just you have set in place a series of actions which resulted in the unintended consequence – bingeing at buffets.

When you repeatedly do things you don't want to do, it is a good idea to look for the pattern which leads up to it. Once you spot it, you will be able to tweak the pattern and change the consequences. In this case, eating normally at buffets.

To see the pattern of what makes you binge at buffets, just ask yourself 2 key questions:

Question One: What am I doing differently when I go to a buffet?

When you are at buffets, do you eat the way you normally do? Do you normally decide what you are going to eat and mysteriously find yourself suddenly eating far more food, even if you are not hungry and not particularly enjoying the food? If the answer is 'No', then ask yourself this,

'What's causing me to eat differently when I go to a buffet?'

Question Two: What did you do differently before the buffet?

How did you eat on the day of the wedding buffet? Most people answer something like this:

'When I got up, I was looking forward to the occasion and the buffet. We weren't invited to the whole of the wedding, just the evening party. Well, I thought I would be overeating at the night, so I just had a light breakfast at about 7:30am. I just had a sandwich for lunch around 12:30 and around 5:00pm started to get ready for the wedding party. We didn't have our tea that night because we would be eating at the buffet. About 7:00pm I went to the party. The rest you know.

Summary

Do you usually eat like this when invited out in the evening? *'Yes.'*
And every time there is a buffet you binge? *'Yes.'*
But when you eat normally, do you ever binge? *'No.'*

So why don't you eat normally during the day, before you go to a buffet? 'Because, I have to make up for the extra food I will eat at the buffet.'

OK, let's look at the pattern that makes you binge at buffets. You get up, have a light breakfast and a sandwich for lunch at 12:30, and then nothing until 8.30pm or later. That's over 8 hours without food. Would you ever normally eat this late? 'No, because I would be starving.'

And when you are starving, are you in a good place to make sensible decisions around food? 'Perhaps not.'

Tweaking the Pattern

How about next time you are invited out in the evening, try eating normally throughout the day and have a snack or sandwich around teatime. Just think of it as having one of the buffet sandwiches a little early. This way, you will be ready to eat when the buffet comes out, but not starving. More importantly, you will be in a better position to choose what to eat and really enjoy what you choose.

Try this small tweak and you will be surprised at how you will not only survive the wedding buffet but really enjoy it.

EVENT RESTRICTION

You know that an event is coming up, like Christmas, where you will most probably over-eat. To make up for it, you eat less in the week (or longer) before the event. You've tried it over and over again and what happens? You find yourself bingeing on everything you can see, eating far more than anyone else, which is followed by the usual feelings of guilt and shame and then the resolution to make up for it the next day.

Take a step back and consider everything you have learned from this book and from your own experience. Basically, you have stepped back into diet mentality. You know now that dieting (restriction) causes bingeing. Event restriction basically sets you up to fail. Don't do that. Think about it: Christmas is a celebration where we have special food and we tend to over-eat. Ask yourself this question: 'Do I deserve to join in the celebration with everyone else?' The answer is, 'Of course you do.' Why not just carry on with the structured eating before the big day and just enjoy the celebration and don't forget to eat breakfast the next day. Trust your body to balance things out over time.

'I had a lovely Christmas and it's the first one in years that I haven't spiraled, binged and put on noticeable weight.

The best thing was I didn't have the urge or feel out of control at any point, which is a massive step in the right direction compared to past years'.

John

HOLIDAYS

The extreme form of event restriction is the build-up for the holidays. From springtime, the magazines are full of advice of how to get your 'beach body' in time for the holidays. So, what happens? People go on a strict diet and throw their body into survival mode, then feel that they have earned the right to eat everything while on holiday.

Here is a typical conversation, with a patient of mine called Claire:

Claire: How come when my friends go on holiday they put on about 2lbs but when I go on holiday I put on at least 10lbs?

Me: What did you do before you went on holiday?

Claire: I went on a diet, of course.

Me: Why did you go on a diet before you went on holiday?

Claire: To make up for all the extra food I would eat on holiday. When I go on holiday, I feel that I have worked hard all year and I really deserve a treat. I like to treat myself without feeling guilty on holiday.

Me: How much weight did you lose before your holiday?

Claire: About 10lbs. **Loud, crashing sound as the penny drops**. Do you mean if I hadn't been on a diet before the holiday, I wouldn't have put so much weight on?

Me: Well, I can't say for sure, but you know that when you lose weight, the first thing you lose is glycogen, which is made up of 3 parts water and 1 part carbohydrate This is why for the first week or two of a diet, it is easy to lose 6lbs to 10lbs in weight. For every 1lb you lose, you also lose 3lbs of water or 4lbs in weight. Unfortunately, when you regain weight, you first replace your glycogen reserves.

This fact is the cause of much distress to many dieters. They go out for a meal and the next day they seem to have put on pounds.

Hence the old advice: 'Always wear your tight clothes on the first week of your holiday, because they will not fit on the second week.' Don't worry, it's just your body keeping you healthy by replenishing your glycogen reservoir.

TAKE-AWAY FOOD

You've got your structured eating under control and your blood sugar levels are stable. Now you want to try to eat a bit more healthily. Say, for example, you think you are eating too many take-away meals and you want to cut back. So, what do you do? Do you go home and announce to your family:

'I want to eat more healthily, I think take-aways are a real problem for me, so from now on let's stop ordering take-away food.'

You look at the fallen faces of your family, which seem to say accusingly, 'You have a problem with food ('You ate all the pies' as they say in the UK.) NOT us. So because of you, we can't have any more delicious take-aways.' As you look at them you realise that's not going to happen.

Let's rewind that and instead say:

'I want to eat more healthily. Take-aways are a real problem for me, so for the next month, how about only have a take-away once a week and you get to choose what type of food?'

In most cases, your partner and family would see this as a reasonable request and go along with it. The key here is that it's time limited (for the next month) and reasonable (once a week) and they get to choose. Put the money you saved on one side and at the end of the month treat the family.

FRIENDS WHO ARE DIETING

You are doing well when suddenly your friend announces that they are going on a diet. Remember that when others go on a diet, they approach it differently and much less seriously than you. Most people will stick at their diet at first, but by week 3 they are generally back to square one. Just let them get on with it and carry on with building your positive habits to achieve your goals.

It's tempting to try to help them avoid the anguish, but try not to get involved. These are adults and it is their right to decide what is best for them. Don't try to convince them that diets don't work. They will probably be all excited about their latest diet and will counter any thoughtful argument you might have with the crass generalisations that they have been peddled for decades. You know the type of stuff – it's a lifestyle change – I'm doing it to get healthier etc

It is difficult to watch friends putting themselves through misery, so you might want to point to relevant sections of this book. But, if they still chose to go on a diet, that's their prerogative, let them get on with it. Be there for them when they fall.

FRIEND LOSES WEIGHT ON A DIET

Barbara has lost a lot of weight and everyone is saying how great she looks. The problem is that this has a tendency to provoke 'beauty and the beast' thinking – 'She looks great, so I must look terrible.' Be alert for this type of thinking; it is common but has no basis in reality.

Ask yourself this: 'Can there be more than one beautiful woman/man in the world/town/room?'

Of course there can. Be happy for them, while it lasts. When you meet this friend, try not to compliment her weight loss, as it only encourages people to equate losing weight to being a better person. Your friend was probably a lovely person before they lost weight and is probably just as lovely now. But don't be churlish. Say something like, 'Oh that must have taken some willpower,' and move on.

FRIEND PUTS WEIGHT BACK ON

Just be sympathetic and point out that diets never worked for you either. For most people this is enough. But if you want to go further, explain how our biology makes long-term weight loss through dieting almost impossible, 95% of people put the weight back on and more. Point to Brownwell's yo-yo dieting rats. Look back at the chapters which show that dieting slows down our metabolism while at the same time makes us hyper alert around food and, sooner or later, dieting ends in a binge. Ask any teacher: in a funny way, explaining things to others can help us to understand a subject at a deeper level. Maybe say that this is good learning for the future etc.

PARTNER WANTS TO LOSE WEIGHT

A client of mine, Jerry, who was recovering from 20 years of binge eating, came home one night and discovered her husband had suddenly decided to lose weight. He was excitedly cooking their evening meal and had cut their carbohydrate portions by half. She decided that she was not going to put her recovery at risk, so she ate her meal and made up for the deficiency by eating extra snacks.

The next day, we met for our appointment and I asked her if he would keep it up for any length of time. She said, 'Oh, it's a big deal now, but this weekend we are going out for a meal with friends and it will all be forgotten.' We talked about how far she had come in her recovery. At one time she would have leapt on any chance to diet. Deep down, she would have known it would have been a short-lived diet for her husband, but she would have taken it far more seriously. Jerry had 20 years of binge eating experience. She put her long-term recovery first and let her husband get on playing at his short-term diet.

Hopefully, these examples are useful in helping handle some difficult situations. Remember, recovery is great. Think about all the extra time, money and energy you can now put into something you are passionate about and making the world a better place.

BITESIZE

In recovery, it is easy to find yourself slipping back into old ways of thinking by real world events. These can catch you out and the surge of emotion that accompanies them can seem overwhelming. However, many of these situations can be anticipated and it is a good idea to have a plan for how to handle such events calmly, before they happen.

I have outlined some of the more common situations:

- The diet expert

- Old thinking bubbles up

- Wedding buffet/eating out

- Event restriction: Christmas/holidays

- Take-away food

- Friend goes on a diet

- Friend loses weight

- Friend puts weight back on

- Partner goes on a diet

These are just a few of the real-world situations that you will have to negotiate in recovery. A little bit of planning will get you out of a lot of potentially difficult situations.

Sit down now and draw up a list of the difficult situations you are likely to meet in the coming months and have a plan of how to skillfully manage them.

MY NOTES

This one's for you

WHAT I LEARNED... WHAT I WILL DO...

CHAPTER SIXTEEN

GETTING THE BEST HELP FROM YOUR GP

When asking for help from a doctor, it is useful to have a little understanding of their role, the constraints they work under and the resources they have at hand.

General Practitioners (GPs) are just that – generalists. That means they know a lot about medicine in general but are usually not experts in any particular area. Their role is to diagnose, prescribe and, where appropriate, refer the patient on to specialist care. In the UK, the average appointment is for 10 minutes.

Speaking from the UK perspective, our GPs (with notable exceptions) are often not au fait with eating disorders. Most have some knowledge about anorexia because they know the suicide risk of anorexia, and to be fair, the provision of care is hit and miss around the country. As for bulimia, they will probably do a blood test, but may have few options for referral. Binge eating is often treated as an obesity problem, i.e. an appointment with the practice nurse who will probably give you a diet sheet.

GP PERSPECTIVE

People don't often seek help when they are coping. It is usually a time of crisis (often after years) when a person finally makes an appointment with the GP.

Look at it from the GP's point of view. They've had a busy day and you walk in in a highly emotional state, saying you have a problem with food and telling them how it is ruling your life. The GP sees a very anxious patient and prescribes something to reduce the anxiety, such as anti-depressants or counselling. Needless to say, this doesn't always go down too well. But from the GP's point of view, it is entirely understandable.

WORK WITH YOUR GP – HELP THEM TO HELP YOU.

As I say, GPs are generalists, but most practices have doctors who have a special interest in certain areas. Ring up the practice and ask if there is a specific doctor who deals with eating disorders. If not, ask who specialises in mental health issues and book an appointment with this doctor.

Do some research, find out what services are available in your area. Write down the information for the doctor.

Take a friend to support you, to take notes of what the GP says and be your advocate. It is often difficult to remember all that the GP says during a consultation and your friend can be a big help.

Be as calm as you can when you are asking for help. State clearly you have an eating disorder and you want help to recover. Ask the GP to refer you to a suitable clinician.

Don't try to justify your claim by saying how bad it is – it will only make you anxious. But answer the GPs questions as objectively as you can.

If the GP says that they will refer you to a dietician, ask to be referred to a dietician with specialist knowledge in eating disorders.

If the GP offers counselling, ask to be referred to a psychotherapist who specialises in eating disorders. Person-centred counselling, while it has its place, is not appropriate for your recovery.

If the GP says there are no specialist services in your area, ask to be referred out of the area to a suitable service.

If possible, take in some materials to help the GP understand your condition. Try to help your GP access the best professional help for you.

It is key that you ask for help, you have a complex condition and some GPs are simply brilliant.

- Work with your doctor. Remember they are generalists and might not have specialist knowledge of eating disorders.

- Bring a friend to take notes and advocate for you.

- Stay calm.

- Ask to be referred to an appropriate clinician with specialist knowledge of eating disorders.

- If there is not suitable service in your area – ask to be referred to a service outside your area.

CHAPTER SEVENTEEN

RESOURCES

I have spent years researching eating disorder: YouTube videos, reading blogs, listening to podcasts and checking out resources on websites (note to self: 'get a life'). I have found some that are brilliant, some mistaken and some downright dangerous. So that you know where to go for the best information and advice, I have drawn up this list of the best, the ones I know my clients find most valuable. All are excellent communicators and my clients find it encouraging to hear the same message, with a slightly different slant, from different people. Plus, they are all on the internet and available anytime you need reassurance that you are doing the right thing.

Some of these resources are by people who have recovered from anorexia, which at first sight seems a world away from bulimia and binge eating. However, without going into the complexities here, they offer lots of insights into the fear of gaining weight, fear of foods, exercise, obsessively thinking about food, body image, and the effects of restriction which are really relevant to you. You don't have to have anorexia to benefit from what these talented people have to say in their own inimitable way.

But before we dive into the resources, here are my thoughts on how to quickly sort out a good from a bad treatment programme.

HOW TO CHOOSE AN EFFECTIVE BULIMIA OR BINGE EATING RECOVERY TREATMENT

There are many people on out there who say they can help you recover from an eating disorder – but can they? If you are looking for a good treatment programme, here are some pointers that will save you a lot of time, money and anguish.

Good treatment programme will consist of:

• structured eating to nourish your body to health.
• flexible rules that are simple and easy to follow.
• skill building to increase your resilience.
• working with you as an individual at your own speed.

- Restrictive eating, often with the promise of weight loss.
- 'Silver Bullet' – show you the one vital secret.
- Expensive and/or secret supplements.
- Over complicated set of 'iron rules' which must be followed to the letter.

If you are looking for a treatment programme, you might find this interview helpful.

Kelly Clark's interview with me about my treatment programme:

Kelly is an eating disorder recovery coach and author of 'It Took Me 10 Years to Lose 10 Pounds. In my interview with Kelly we discuss the various aspects of the treatment programme I use with my clients. There are many aspects to an eating disorder – physical, psychological and emotional – but this interview concentrates on how we end the diet/binge cycle that results in Food Chaos. In the interview, Kelly talks from her own experience of how structured eating was the basis of her recovery.

https://www.the10principles.com/structured-eating-helped-me-lose-weight/

BACKGROUND RESOURCES:

There are many people on out there who say they can help you recover from an eating disorder – but can they? If you are looking for a good treatment programme, here are two resources about the influence of the cult of thinness on our culture. The first shows the truth about the latest fad, 'clean eating' and the second is an exhortation to stop worrying about your weight and start living.

The Truth About Clean Eating: clean eating's dirty secrets

Grace Victory investigates what is peddled over the internet as clean eating. This is an informative documentary (approximately 35 mins) which shows how clean eating has been distorted from good initial intentions into a money-making industry.

Grace tries some of the recommendations to hilarious effect. But can we trust them, these self-appointed experts? Grace actually asks dieticians to comment on claims such as 'don't drink milk, it draws calcium from our bones resulting in calcium deficit' hmm…. can you imagine what the dietician said? Watch this – you'll love it.

https://youtu.be/MUeNab6-C7U

When you own your Belly Jelly

Here is a group of women who are not falling into the trap of trying to gain an unattainable body shape before getting on and enjoying their lives. Do you want to argue with them? Er, feel free – I don't! (approximately 1 min 30 secs).

https://youtu.be/Qubij4Fo3Rs

EATING DISORDER RESOURCES

Millstone – eating disorders as they are lived
If you have every tried to tell someone what it is like to have an eating disorder and they just don't get it, get them to watch this short film (approximately 30 mins). If you are having problems with your GP, having difficulty explaining how you feel, get them to watch this short film.
This remarkable film by 'Men Get Eating Disorders Too' simply lays out just what it feels like to suffer with an eating disorder and the tragic effects that can happen.

https://youtu.be/iRim224xFjE

Treating bulimia: Step 1: this is the first step in becoming a normal eater
This short video (approximately 8 mins) from Shaye Boddington from http://www.your-bulimia-recovery.com highlights the importance of structured eating in bulimia and binge eating recovery. In a previous video Shaye explains how the biggest mistake people make when trying to recover is to skip this stage. But without structured eating most recovery attempts are

doomed to fail. Here Shaye explains just what this vital first step involves.

https://youtu.be/JuyjhTED4ek.

The secret way to eat fewer calories
Worried about gaining weight by structured eating? Let me introduce you to Lydia Wente. Lydia is a bit whacky for some tastes but go with it. It's less than 2 minutes long and she makes a really good point. I show this to all my clients, and they all love it.

https://youtu.be/5fKXJIHQvDU

CREDIBLE WEBSITES

National Centre for Eating Disorders
https://eating-disorders.org.uk
Lots of really good information about the various eating disorders and their treatment from an expert, Deanne Jade, Founder and Principal.

BEAT eating disorders
https://www.beateatingdisorders.org.uk
UK eating disorders charity offering information, help finding support groups and a helpline.

The Eating Disorder Institute
https://edinstitute.org
If you like rigorous scientific analysis, this is the place for you. Gwyneth Olwyn writes a no-nonsense manner that takes no prisoners and, if you want to sort the facts from the fiction, a great site. I would advise any medic with an interest in disordered eating to become acquainted with this site. For a taste of the style, I would advise you to read 'Dear Doctor, your patient has an eating disorder'

https://edinstitute.org/paper/2016/2/13/dear-doctor-your-patient-has-an-eating-disorder?rq=doctor

KELLY CLARK — THE 10 PRINCIPLES
http://www.the10principles.com
I have been a fan of Kelly's for years now. She consistently comes up with great information in a really accessible and fun way. Kelly speaks from the

heart and what she says it simply brilliant. If you follow just one blog, make sure it is Kelly's

https://www.the10principles.com/structured-eating-helped-me-lose-weight/

Have a look around Kelly's site, I am sure parts of it will resonate. To start I would recommend:

Stop grazing
This is a brilliant blog by Kelly Clark from www.the10principles.com Kelly spent 10 years of restricting her diet and carrying out a punishing exercise regime. She finished up basically not eating meals but grazing through the day. But no matter how hard she tried, she was always between 10 and 30lbs overweight. In this blog Kelly tells how she took on the identity of 'someone who was a grazer', how grazing makes your bulimia or binge eating worse, how once she started eating meals again and finally, how as well of getting her life back, she actually lost weight once she started eating normally.

www.the10principles.com/grazing/

Slow Metabolism
Kelly explains that for years she thought she had a slow metabolism. This blog explains how to work with your body to get your slow metabolism to bounce back.

http://www.the10principles.com/slow-metabolism/

Stop bingeing
This blog explains why we over-eat and how the starve - binge - purge cycle makes you gain weight. More importantly, it shows you how to break this cycle in three steps and get your life back.

http://www.the10principles.com/stop-binging/

Kelly's structured eating plan
After years of under-eating, eating what can seem like a lot more food can be very scary. It was for Kelly. In this blog she explains how she started with what she could stand to eat and built up on that.

https://www.the10principles.com/break-the-cycle/

Tabitha Farrar
Tabitha has a no-nonsense attitude to eating disorders. Tabitha has also recovered from anorexia and, like Sarah, lots of what she talks about is directly relevant to recovering from binge eating and bulimia. For example, if you have had an eating disorder for several years, you might not be able to remember what life is like without it. Knowing what freedom from your conditions would be like is very motivating. Listen to this podcast where Tabitha answers a question from one of her clients by musing on her life before recovery vs after recovery. She covers areas of life such as:
• **Dining out**
• **Social life**
• **Exercise**
• **Feeling cold**

https://tabithafarrar.com/2017/10/recovery-vs-recovery/

Tabitha writes brilliant blogs: https://tabithafarrar.com/blog/
Answers questions on her YouTube Channel: https://youtu.be/5s351A5_fl0
Has a great podcast: https://eatingdisorderrecoverypodcast.podbean.com

The Free Eater
https://everythingedrecovery.com
This is a website by Sarah Frances Young. Sarah has recovered from anorexia, but where she talks about fear, thinking styles, eating more and exercising less, body image etc. is directly applicable to people with bulimia and binge eating. Sarah has many videos on her YouTube channel, which is personable. Here she talks about breaking eating disorder habits

https://youtu.be/TSX1KuETIbA

Sarah now puts a lot of her energy into Instagram – look for 'bodypositivepear'.

SUPPORT FOR PARENTS OF CHILDREN WITH AN EATING DISORDER.

FEAST
https://www.feast-ed.org
Support for parents of children with an eating disorder. Some great advice about how to help your child.

Eva Musby
When your loved one suffers from an eating disorder, how to support them.
https://youtu.be/2O9nZAWCkLc

This short animation is a great resource to help you have a better understanding of how your loved one experiences their eating disorder. It will take a lot off your shoulders and help you support your loved one.

I have probably missed off some of the excellent communicators on eating disorders. If so, I apologise. But these resources are a good place to start.

If I have missed any of your favourites, please contact me and let me know on

drtonyhenshall @gmail.com

↑

That's me !

MY NOTES

This one's for you

WHAT I LEARNED... WHAT I WILL DO...

REGAINING
YOUR APPETITE
FOR LIFE

Congratulations, you have now completed the recovery programme that I use with my private clients. By now you know:

• **how eating disorders develop.**
• **how eating disorders affect your life.**
• **what keeps eating disorders firmly in place.**

These are complex conditions, but the first place to start is to tackle Food Chaos. You now have the food knowledge you need and you know how to break the restrict/binge cycle by stabilising your blood sugar levels using structured eating and finding out what works for you using your Food and Mood Diary.

Once your body is stabilised you will be in a better place to tackle the other aspects that keep an eating disorder in place. You now know techniques to deal with:

• **the critical voice**
• **your emotions around food**
• **poor body image**
• **bulimia**
• **relapse prevention**
• **real world problems**

This book has also provided advice on:

• **how friends and family can help, and**
• **getting the best from your GP**

You also have lots of resources to help you work towards your recovery.

NEXT STEPS – ACTIONS SPEAK LOUDER THAN WORDS

You have all the knowledge and skills to recover but it is only you who can make it happen. Turn your knowledge into action. It can all seem daunting, but it isn't really. All you have to do is to start at the beginning and move forward one step at a time. What you don't yet know is that you will learn so much from every step you take.

Start at the beginning now – with Structured Eating. For some, this will take a little planning to make sure you have all the food you need in the house for 3 meals and 3 snacks a day. Simply start from where you are now. It doesn't have to be perfect because, as I have said throughout the book, we are looking for

Improvement NOT Perfection

But until you take action, nothing will change. What are you waiting for? It is time to make a difference and live your life to its full potential.

This is what recovery looks like for Jean:

"For part of the holiday we were with my relations and they are all very slim. I observed how obsessed THEY all were about what they ate, how much they ate, how they berated themselves and the vows they made to eat less the next day.

That's been me in the past!

I didn't engage in any conversation about it with them, it was just quite powerful to observe the things they said.

I can now observe from a position of neutrality & confidence in myself. The pain and sensitivity I used to feel has gone!

I almost laughed out loud at one point as I realised that here's me, overweight and now for once in my life perfectly accepting of myself and who I am and I was sat with these beautiful, slim women who couldn't let go and just enjoy eating without all these issues and self judgements without worrying that they would put weight on. It's ludicrous. I felt proud to be me & proud of breaking those chains

And whilst they were worrying about what they were eating, I just enjoyed myself. I went off, running round being daft with me kids in the garden and loved it."

CONTACT ME

I would love to know how you get on with the programme. You can contact me through my website:

www.drtonyhenshall.com

Facebook: https://www.facebook.com/downwithdiets/
Instagram: https://www.instagram.com/drtonyhenshall
Twitter: @tonyhenshal1
Pinterest: https://www.pinterest.co.uk/drtonyhenshall/pins/

So, what are you waiting for? Good luck and, once you have put this behind you, have fun putting all your talents, skills and energy into something interesting – for the rest of your life ;0)

MY PLAN

This one's for you

WHAT ARE THE PRACTICAL STEPS I CAN START TODAY?

ACKNOWLEDGEMENTS

Although I have written this book, it simply would not have happened without a group of talented people who have helped me every step of the way. Writing a book needs focus and I am notorious for being distracted by any 'shiny objects' that might appear. So I would like to thank this group of women who have 'held my feet to the fire' in order that I finish the book.

I would like to thank Siân-Elin Flint-Freel, my book mentor, without whom this would never have happened. Sian has used all her skills to help me first of all finish my first draft and then to transform it into a book. Thanks Sian, it's been a blast.

I would also like to thank the very talented Natalie McLetchie, who is responsible for the cover and the illustrations throughout the book as well as typesetting the whole thing. I don't know where you get your ideas from – but I'm glad you do.

I would also like to thank my partner, Karen who, unlike me, is very focused and has held me to account every step of the way. Herding cats comes to mind.

Special thanks go to Kelly Clark, a recovery coach, whose work has helped my clients by explaining complex concepts in an easy-to-understand way. I have used many of her clear explanations and some of her techniques. Thanks, Kelly.

I would also like to mention my beta readers who have spent their time helping me to improve my book. I really appreciate your contributions.

Finally, I would like to thank Deanne Jade, the Founder and Principal of the National Centre for Eating Disorders. It was Deanne's training that first sparked my interest in eating disorders and a great deal of what you will read in the book is based on her teaching.

But most of all I would like to thank my lovely clients. Without exception, a wonderful group of people. You have taught me so much and it has been a real privilege getting to know all of you and watching you blossom.

I can't thank you all enough ;) Tony

ABOUT TONY HENSHALL

Tony Henshall has 20 years' experience in helping people to overcome lifestyles and habits detrimental to their health. For the past 5 years, he has been changing lives by guiding clients through his Recovery Programme.

Here is what he has to say about what drew him to helping people who were suffering with binge eating and bulimia, which eventually led to him writing this book:

"In 2000 the UK's National Health Service created services to help smokers quit. I was appointed as a Public Health Specialist Smoking Cessation Advisor. I started from scratch and soon I was seeing the most heavily addicted smokers, smokers with critical health issues, smokers who were told that they couldn't have a life-saving heart bypass unless they quit. It didn't take long before I realised that most of the people I saw had a psychological dependency on nicotine and were self-medicating (or thought they were) anxiety and/or depression with cigarettes.

So, I developed a series of techniques to rapidly relieve stress and anxiety. After teaching these techniques to my smokers, a large majority of them quit the habit.

By 2003 I thought: Well that's smoking done. What's the next big thing? (I know – what was I thinking?)

Obesity was becoming more of a problem in the UK, so I approached my boss and said something along the lines: Smoking is basically all in the head of the smoker (a psychological dependency). We now have the skills to sort that out, why not do the same for obesity? In my naivety, I thought obesity was also a form of psychological dependency. All we needed to do was get a bit of training on obesity and we could add to this the skills developed by working with smokers to form an effective obesity service.

WHAT FOLLOWED WAS LIFE CHANGING.

I took a course on obesity taught by Deanne Jade at the National Centre for Eating Disorders. It soon became apparent that yes, obesity was all in the head, but not as I'd imagined. Rather than a purely psychological issue, obesity was also a biological issue. If you don't eat enough you will not have enough building blocks to make the serotonin or beta endorphins needed for a calm and confident life.

The scales fell from my eyes and I thought: It's not fair. We've been lied to.

Anyone who goes on a restrictive diet is bound to fail and probably put on more weight.

From then on, I've been fascinated (some would say obsessed) by disordered eating and the more I understood what was going on, the madder I got. It's just not fair

It's unfair that we are consistently being bombarded with unrealistic body images that nobody (including the models in the photographs) can attain.

It's unfair that we have conflated good health with an unrealistic idea of thinness and poor health with anything else.

It's unfair that we have been told the way to lose weight is to diet – the very method that is almost certainly guaranteed to make dieters gain weight. Then, when the inevitable rebound weight gain occurs, they blame themselves and not the method for failure.

But what I think is most unfair is that the nicest people, the ones with the characteristics of discipline, willpower, delayed gratification, and striving to do their very best, combined with sensitivity, make these people most vulnerable to eating disorders.

These admirable qualities are the very ones that can spiral into an eating disorder and keep it firmly in place for years and even decades. Such people can restrict their diet harder, exercise harder and stick at it for longer. When the inevitable happens – they fall harder, feel the failure much more deeply and much longer. Instead of just giving up, they get even more motivated to diet and exercise even harder and so the vicious binge/restriction cycle starts again, spiraling down and down.

But getting mad is easy – doing something about it is what counts. This book draws on my knowledge, skills and experience and is my attempt to do something about it, to free people from the tyranny of their eating disorder so they can use their talents to bring something positive into the world.

What I do know is that the road to complete recovery is not difficult – the difficulty is that it is counterintuitive to all the dieting myths that have seeped so deeply into our culture. Giving people the knowledge and confidence to start along the road to recovery and holding their nerve as they make progress is extremely challenging. This book is my contribution to helping people along that road.

The reason I know you can fully recover from Bulimia, Binge Eating and Emotional Eating is that I have seen the proof with my own eyes. Throughout the book you will have heard the voices of my wonderful clients talking of their experiences as they worked towards recovery. They have taught me so much and it has been a privilege for me to watch them bloom and use their talents to flourish.

I now split my time between Manchester and Cheshire, with my partner Karen and the formidable Bob, my moody Lhasa Apso. I take on a number of private clients each year. For more information visit my website or get in touch.

Dr. Tony Henshall

THE EATING DISORDER EXPERT

WWW.DRTONYHENSALL.COM

APPENDIX 1: MEAL SUGGESTIONS

If you are still a little unsure what counts as a snack or what to eat for breakfast, lunch or dinner, I have put together some suggestions to get you started. Remember these are only suggestions, not another set of rules.
Pick the ones that

1) you like to eat and
2) are practical given your life circumstances.

Try them and use your Food and Mood diary to see what works for you.

Meal suggestions
Breakfast - small meal

½ grapefruit
1 boiled egg
2 slices of wholemeal bread or toast
(spread from allowance)

1 glass (100ml) orange juice
2 Weetabix or 2 Shredded Wheat
200ml milk

2 rashers 50g/2oz grilled lean bacon
grilled tomatoes
2 slices of bread or 1 teacake

50g of All Bran or Bran Flakes or
Cornflakes
1 small banana
20ml milk

1 bowl 200g porridge (½ milk, ½ water)
1 slice of wholemeal/white toast butter

grapefruit segments in fruit juice
1 boiled egg
2 slices of wholemeal bread or toast
with Marmite 1 glass (200ml) milk

2 slices of wholemeal/white toast and butter

200g boil in the bag haddock fillets
1 slice of wholemeal/white toast

100g kippers grilled or boiled in the bag
1 slice wholemeal/white bread and butter

50g muesli
200ml milk

4 Ryvita & Marmite and/or 100g cottage cheese

5 prunes in natural juices mixed with 12g Bran Flakes and natural yoghurt

200g fruit salad & 125g natural yoghurt or fromage frais

1 small glass (100ml) fruit juice
175g baked beans on 1 slice of wholemeal/white toast

Snack Meals

cheese on toast
melt 25g hard cheese on 1 slice of
toast. Add tomatoes and onions
2 fresh fruits

mushroom omelette
2 egg omelette with mushrooms
serve with salad and dressing
1 slice of wholemeal/white bread and
butter

jacket potato
1 medium potato with 100g cottage
cheese or 100g baked beans
2 fresh fruits

burger
100g / 1/4lb grilled beef burger in a
bun with salad and 1 tsp of ketchup

fish fingers
4 grilled fish fingers
100g mashed potatoes
100g vegetables
1 tsp ketchup

sardines on toast
100g sardines in tomato sauce
1 slice of wholemeal/white bread
1 yoghurt

sandwiches
2 slices of wholemeal bread or
1 pitta or 1 balm cake and butter

fillings
25g corned beef & beetroot or pickle
50g tuna and sliced tomato and onion
25g ham and mustard and salad
25g cheese and onion
25g roast beef and horseradish sauce
25g roast chicken and salad

Light Main Meal

2 fish cakes baked in the oven or grilled
green vegetables
125g mashed or jacket potato
1 fresh fruit or small yoghurt

100g cod in parsley sauce
100g green vegetables
125g mashed or jacket potato
1 fresh fruit or small yoghurt

75g lean lamb or pork chop

125g mashed or jacket potato
large helping of mixed vegetables
1 fresh fruit or small yoghurt

75g roast chicken
125g jacket potato
green vegetables
1 fresh fruit or small yoghurt
100g grilled sirloin steak
125g jacket potato

grilled tomatoes/mushrooms
mixed salad with dressing
bowl of strawberries

2 grilled sausages
2 tablespoons baked beans
1 slice toast/bread
1 fresh fruit or small yoghurt

150g smoked haddock (poached)
100g mashed potatoes
green vegetables
1 fresh fruit

75g lean stewing steak as beef
casserole
green and root vegetables
200g jacket potato
200g melon

150g gammon steak grilled
100g oven chips
green vegetables/grilled tomatoes
1 fresh fruit

100g braised liver in gravy
large helping assorted vegetables
150g jacket potato
200g tined fruit in fruit juice

100g chicken curry
150g boiled rice
1 grilled popadom and 1 tsp mango
chutney
1 small fruit yoghurt

100g lean minced beef as chill con-
carne
100g boiled rice
50g red kidney beans
1 small fromage frais

300g lasagne
green mixed salad with oil-free dressing
75g crusty bread 100g lean roast beef/
pork/lamb with gravy

brussels sprouts, swedes and
carrots
150g boiled potatoes
1 small fromage frais
1 small banana

100g lean minced beef as in a
cottage pie
200g boiled potatoes (mashed)
assorted mixed vegetables
1 fresh fruit

150 chicken breast/leg as in a
casserole
green and root vegetables
200g new boiled potatoes
150g grapes

100g lean minced beef in spaghetti
Bolognese
150g spaghetti
1 large banana

150g oily fish - salmon, trout,
herring or mackerel mixed salad with
dressing
150g new boiled potatoes
2 small fromage frais

250g white fish grilled or poached
with 2 tbsp of parsley sauce
mixed vegetables
150g boiled or jacket potato
50g vanilla ice cream

Main Meals

175 lean roast beef/lamb/pork with gravy
large helping of mixed vegetables
200g boiled or jacket potato
125g frozen yoghurt

100g lean minced beef as in chilli con carne
100g boiled or jacket potato
large helping of mixed vegetables
1 banana chopped with custard 100g stewing steak as in beef casserole
200g boiled or jacket potatoes
large helping of assorted vegetables
1 banana chopped with custard

Light Vegetarian

175g bean and vegetable stew
200g egg noodles (boiled)
100g fruit salad in fruit juice

175g vegetarian cottage pie
200g boiled mashed potatoes
1 small fruit yoghurt

100g thin based vegetarian pizza
50g vanilla ice cream
100g fresh strawberries/raspberries
100g vegetarian chilli
100g boiled brown rice
1 fresh fruit

calorie value of some vegetarian foods

50g lentils (dry weight) - 150 cals
100g tofu - 100 cals
100g cooked beans - kidney, mung, black eye, butter, aduki or chick peas - 100 cals

Snacks

Larger snacks

1 large thick slice of toast
200g baked beans
1 fresh fruit

300ml tined vegetable soup
2 large thick slices of toast and
butter

2 thick slices wholemeal or granary
bread
100g cottage cheese with chives

200g jacket potato
200g baked beans

4 Ryvita and Marmite
2 hard boiled eggs

2 large thick slices of toast
200g tinned spaghetti in tomato
sauce

1 cup of soup
2 large thick slices wholemeal/white
bread and butter
50g tuna and chopped tomato

Light snacks

25g cheddar on 1 Ryvita
1 toasted crumpet and butter
125g grapes
1 large banana
1 small fruit yoghurt
1 small fruit fromage frais
1 cereal bar
1 slice of wholemeal bread or toast
and butter
3 Rich Tea biscuits
2 small Digestive biscuits
4 crisp breads
1 apple and 1 pear or peach
1 fun sized Milky Way
2 bar Kit Kat

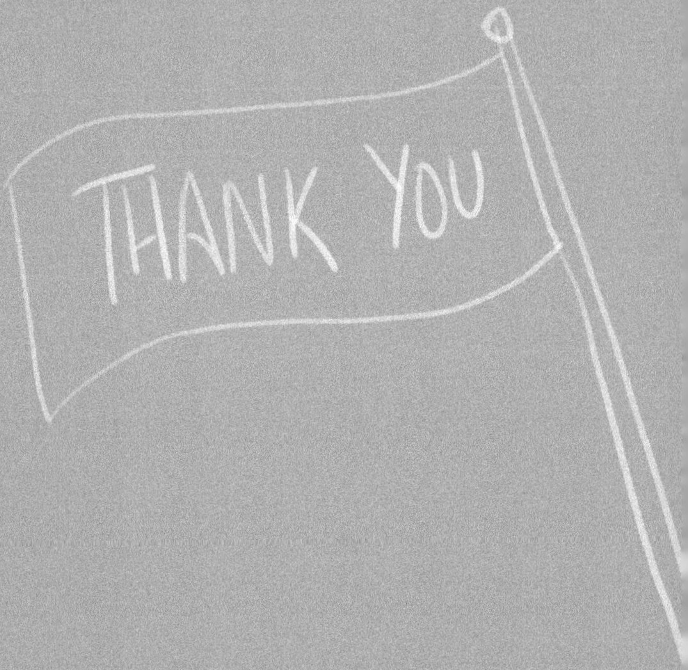
THANK YOU